Living in a Bubble

A Guide to being diagnosed with
High Functioning Asperger's as an Adult

Anthony King

Published by Faria Publishing Limited 2019

Living in a Bubble: A Guide to being diagnosed with High Functioning Asperger's as an Adult, by Anthony King (First Edition)

Edited by Debz Hobbs-Wyatt
Formatted by Polgarus Studio

ISBN: 978-1-9996049-6-7 (print)
ISBN: 978-1-9996049-7-4 (eBook)

I dedicate this book to my dear friends,
Nicky and Collin

Contents

Introduction

My name's Anthony King. If you're reading this book it's likely that you've been diagnosed with "High Functioning Asperger's" (HFA) or "Autism Spectrum Disorder" (ASD) or you believe you might be on the spectrum. According to the National Autistic Society (NAS), of the United Kingdom there are around 700,000 people in the UK living with autism – that's more than 1 in 100 of us (this includes Asperger's Syndrome and all those with autism). That's a lot of us... **you are not alone.**

I feel privileged to connect with you. Think of it as going on a journey together.

I see it as you inviting me into your world, so please do something for me. Imagine that every time you read this book I am a friend sitting with you, speaking directly to you. If you don't mind, take me to your "safe space", that place where you can relax and be yourself. Maybe it's a certain spot in a park under the tree, maybe it's in your bedroom, maybe it's in a museum – invite me there and let's talk.

You might also be a "special interest", which means that you might be a partner, parent, or friend of someone on the spectrum ... and you too are welcome. I ask that you be with us as an observer – completely detached and non-judgemental. You have full permission to "eavesdrop" on our conversation but please remember: be respectful. Your role is just as valuable and special and the fact that you are taking the time to understand this subject is an honour, so thank you. Now I'm going to speak with YOU.

Let me say again: you are not alone. However, I totally understand that you might initially feel sceptical. At this point in your life you may feel extremely alone and the four words, "you", "are", "not" and "alone" certainly doesn't change that. They're just words but this a turning point in your life. I am going to assume that life has sometimes been a challenge and often confusing. Living with ASD, in my opinion, can be one of the loneliest places, but I want to assure you that I have walked the same path as you. I want you to know that I know how you feel and I am thinking about you and these words are going to help you. If nothing else, you will realise that there are others who walk the same road and can help.

When I was diagnosed I had mixed emotions that were hard to quantify. The overwhelming feeling was *that I was alone*. I left the doctor, who was incredibly kind, with the feeling that I wasn't in need of any particular medical attention. I needed someone or something to give me a little encouragement and point me in the right direction. I didn't have anybody.

I initially read everything I could on the internet. Most of it was hurtful and appalling. I called up the autism charity helpline a couple of times but it was always engaged. I then decided to purchase some books but I was in for a surprise... there was hardly anything relevant to me. There was lots of parenting advice for children on the spectrum; lots of books about young teens on the spectrum; but not a lot for an adult who'd just been diagnosed. I found text books and science books but nothing relevant for me. What I needed was something personal, something that would give me a little encouragement at a confusing time. There was no doubt that, ultimately, I would be alright but during that time I needed something I couldn't find. So I decided to write that book.

I wanted to write a book which included information about traits and important things to look out for based on personal experience, my own coping techniques and practical ways of helping. In a way this is a self-help book but I hope a little more personal than a textbook. I also wanted to tell you about how ASD has affected my life and how I've interpreted those experiences through the lens of Asperger's. It's very possible that you will relate because you have gone through similar experiences.

In a nutshell, with this book: if I am talking about it, it means that I have experienced it. If I am telling a story, it means that it is real and actually happened. I will change names but the stories themselves are real.

This book will give you hope. The techniques really work. I am here to deliver good news.

I'm going to say the words "you are not alone" one more time at the end of this book. Compare how you feel *then*, to how you feel *now*. Let's start at the beginning …

Anthony King

Chapter 1

What is Autism Spectrum Disorder/High Functioning Asperger's?

When I initially sat my friends down and told them I have ASD the first thing they asked (with a strange look on their face) was "What's that?"

My answer, which I wasn't particularly at ease or satisfied with was this:

> *"It means that I interact with the world differently and I'm often challenged and affected by things which "normal" people don't notice, like certain sounds and noise. These, in particular, can cause me significant pain and distress. I also feel like an alien, like I don't fit in because I can find it hard to understand people and translate what they really mean. It just takes me a little bit more time to decode because I do things by calculation rather than by intuition. I've trained myself to do this which is why I can blend in and most people wouldn't notice.*

However, on the inside it can be hard, exhausting and this is why I like to spend time by myself and to recuperate after certain situations."

This might not be the best description; which is why I sometimes add, "I just find things that normal people do naturally challenging at times." I fortunately have an opportunity right now to answer the question properly. So here goes…

Autism Spectrum Disorder and Asperger's Syndrome

Let me clarify something important about terminology. There have been recent changes to the medical diagnostic manuals which means that a condition which was once called "Asperger's Syndrome" is now classed under the wider title of "Autism Spectrum Disorder". However, some people who were diagnosed before the diagnostic change still officially have "Asperger's Syndrome" and others, after, have "Autism Spectrum Disorder". Doctors and specialists will often describe the condition as "Asperger's" or "Autism" or "Autism Spectrum Disorder". So from this point on, I will mostly refer to the condition that encompasses all of these things under one umbrella as "Autism

Spectrum Disorder" abbreviated to ASD, or as 'on the spectrum'.

So, what is ASD?

Put simply, ASD is described as a "lifelong developmental disability". However, it's a part of your identity. It can't be "cured", you don't "heal". It's not a disease either. It doesn't come with any kind of learning difficulties per se but someone with ASD may have a specific learning difficulty. Many autistic people, on the other hand, do have learning difficulties and challenges with communication and speech (which people with ASD can also have) but people with ASD can often, as I said above, have difficulty "decoding" or processing and understanding language and speech.

One thing I can say is that with help, assistance and looking within, people on the spectrum can have a fulfilled and happy life.

What is "High functioning Asperger's"?

It's logical that some people have a more extreme condition than others but ASD is not a "spectrum" disorder in the way that people often interpret the word "spectrum". People have wrongly suggested that since I am not an "extreme" case, I don't have a problem. Not at all. I still have it, just in a different way to some.

Those with the "High Functioning" form have the ability to blend in and fit in through different coping mechanisms – it might not even be obvious, but it's still there.

What is the cause of ASD and is there a cure?

Scientists still haven't found a "cure" because they have not been able to attribute an exact cause. Current research suggests it is probably a combination of factors: environmental and genetic, working together. One thing is certain – it isn't anybody's fault. While there is no current cure, there are many ways to make life easier – such as employing specific coping strategies and resolving challenging issues.

How many people have ASD?

To reiterate my findings, according to the NAS, of the United Kingdom there are around 700,000 people in the UK living with autism – that's more than 1 in 100. They come from all walks of life. Statistics suggest that more males than females are affected.

What specific challenges do people with ASD face when interacting?

The world can often be a very overwhelming place to live when you're on the spectrum. This can cause stress and anxiety. Interacting with other people, including communication, interpretation, interaction (socially and in other ways) can be confusing and challenging. People on the spectrum often feel misunderstood, scared, ignored and like they don't fit in. This can be compounded psychologically because you often can't tell by looking at somebody or even interacting with them superficially whether they have ASD. Young children on the spectrum can be perceived as just "naughty".

Social interaction and communication

People on the autistic spectrum often have difficulties interpreting things. For example, tone of voice, subtext, non-verbal and verbal communication and often take things literally, which can make it hard to understand certain types of sarcasm, expressions, phrases and jokes. It's best to speak with somebody on the spectrum directly and clearly – although many people on the spectrum have a good grasp of sarcasm and are very humorous. Another thing which is quite common is for those with ASD to speak about the same thing a lot, often repeating themselves or what others have said. They might talk at length about their special interests (and usually have very good language skills) and sometimes need more time than other people to process and interpret what they have heard.

This is why it's usually important to speak in a direct, clear and consistent way to somebody on the spectrum because they might have difficulty in reading or recognising what's going on inside the other person's head, if it is not clearly stated. People with ASD might not recognise indicators and cues for emotions and feelings which can make it hard to interact with the world. Consequently, they may find it hard to make friends and form relationships and maintain them because they might appear to be insensitive and often reclusive or eccentric. Sometimes people with ASD want to make friends but just don't know how.

The three Rs – Rituals, Repetitive and Routines

A person with Asperger's will often have a routine or routines that can seem quite ritualistic. This is because it gives a little form and control to an often unpredictable and stressful environment. At least with a personal routine you can create the circumstances that you do control and can derive comfort from that. Repetitive behaviour might include eating the same meals at the same time every day, or sitting in the same chair on the train every day or dressing in the same type of clothes. A person with ASD is often more comfortable with rules and a framework which they can get used to because change can often be hard to process. Although, with prior notice and preparation, change can be more easily accepted.

Obsessions and special interests

Many of us on the spectrum have a special interest (or many special interests), which we have focussed on with a certain level of obsessiveness. This can be an unusual (possibly perceived as eccentric) talent like a musical instrument or learning about something; anything from aeroplanes to windmills! This level of focus and obsessiveness can often translate with the right assistance and direction into being an expert in certain areas or subjects.

Sensory issues (sound, light, smell etc.)

A particular issue for me, and many others with ASD, is sensitivity to certain sounds, noises and smells. This sensitivity means that a noise which most people might ignore can be painful and cause headaches and an inability to focus. Many people with ASD also have sensitivity to light which makes it hard for them too.

All I ever read is, 'Tips for parents with children with autism' but what about us? What about adults on the spectrum who need some help and advice? So after exploring the areas outlined in more detail I will offer some practical advice for us, as adults, too.

Chapter 2

Discovering I was on the Spectrum

Never would I ever have thought that I would be diagnosed with ASD. My whole life only two people had ever suggested it, and that was as a joke.

Why? Because they saw me as different perhaps?

Was it my talent? I *was* perceived as an eccentric but this worked really well for me. It gave me a "reason" for my uniqueness. I was unusually talented; people recognised that talent and this gave me artistic license to be classed as an "eccentric artist" instead of anything else. I could be a recluse; I could just work on my craft for months on end; I could keep myself to myself; speak differently; act differently; dress differently and it was all fine – I was an "artiste".

This way of thinking isn't necessarily incorrect. However, it didn't properly address the issue. I knew something was different – and I needed to know what.

This longing for truth and my insatiable curiosity are what eventually led me to look into ASD. That's when I realised the signs had all been there – I just hadn't seen them.

I want to paint

I have always had the ability to teach myself skills. I like the process of learning something new. Society at large doesn't like it when we do this. It makes people uncomfortable. They want their accountants to be "accountants" rather than an accountant who plays in a rock band, whose second hobby is base jumping off mountains! However, there is a fun aspect to the challenge of learning something from scratch. It was actually something beyond my control with a theatre that led me to have to frustratingly cancel a show, that led me to look at alternative venues, leading me to a gallery which gave me the idea to paint a painting ... something which was totally new to me!

After the disappointment of the cancelled show, my creative juices were once again flowing and I thought that if I was going to perform in a gallery possibly, it would be fun to create some art to exhibit during the performance. I was a professional dancer, performer and choreographer. I could play musical instruments, sing and I could write books... but this was something totally new that I would have to learn from scratch.

I was away! I had the name, I had the concept and I even had some of the music composed in my head already. There was only one thing I didn't have a clue about – the art! In fact, I didn't even know if I could paint. But I knew that the ability was inside me to learn. So the first thing I did was to Google oil paintings. I noticed that a lot of information was contradictory or focussed in a simple way. I wanted to know more about the challenge and if it was possible for me so I went to the book shop and purchased five books on oil painting. They all made it look pretty romantic and easy, so I thought I would definitely go ahead.

A few days later I discovered there was an art shop very close to the dance studio. I decided to make my way there immediately. No point in delaying. A very helpful lady assisted me. She then took me around the shop and we picked up everything a beginner needs. I set them up and waited for the right moment to see if I had any talent.

I created a very long Erik Satie playlist, put the music

on, put my rubber gloves on, set up all the equipment and proceeded. It was a little more complicated to mix the paints and the special liquids than I thought but I just went with it. I wanted to paint a Paris cityscape, so I just started painting straight onto the canvas.

I hated it.

I thought it looked awful. I carried on for about thirty minutes and then decided that painting wasn't for me.

I went to bed disappointed. The next day I woke up again to the same beautiful sun. As I always did when I woke up, I'd put on Erik Satie and then make a cup of tea, walk out to the balcony windows and just look and absorb the city. I saw the easel still set up and thought to myself, "Practice makes perfect and you are going to paint a finished piece no matter what." With renewed motivation I changed the original slightly, from a very complicated Paris street scene to a simpler street scene.

With Erik Satie's beautiful piano music accompanying me, I painted. This time I felt connected. I was enjoying it. This was my first time and I didn't care how it looked in the end, I was going to try my best. I painted half the painting that day. I let it dry for a couple of days. Then I finished it in about thirty minutes a few days later. For a first ever oil painting it didn't look too bad. It didn't look amazing but for a first piece, even I saw potential. I knew that if I continued, by my hundredth painting I would have improved considerably.

That evening I went to bed late (normal for me) and I couldn't sleep. I used that quiet time to read and to think and educate myself. I was thinking about the idea that if you don't try, you won't succeed. For some reason, the idea the three words "London art competitions" came into my head. I thought I'd Google it and I happened upon a famous gallery in central London, right near Buckingham Palace, on the Mall. I noticed that nearly all of the competitions had been open for months and months and had already closed.

As I went to click off the page, I noticed something at the bottom, "New England Art Open Competition". I looked at the closing date for submissions and I noticed that it was in forty-eight hours' time… actually less, because it was 4am! I looked up the requirements and thought to myself, "What have I got to lose?" I decided to submit my painting and I thought it was really funny. The next day I photographed the painting, filled in all the forms, paid the fee and emailed it off. I expected (and rightfully so!) that I would receive a rejection email.

The response email said that they could not take all entries but that they would consider all entries and that they would put the first selection up on their website and entrants should check to see if they got through or not. Only the ones selected would have their number shown. At this stage I basically forgot about it. I thought there was no chance. It was my first painting, painted on a whim.

A few weeks later the results were to be announced. If we had been selected we had to have our canvases especially framed (with lots of specifications and requirements) and hand deliver them to the gallery on a certain day. On that day the results were to be announced at midday so I wasn't expecting the email that arrived just after 9am which basically said "Dear Anthony, congratulations on being pre-selected. Frame your painting and drop it off to the gallery, you're through to the next round".

I was gobsmacked!

Getting it framed proved more problematic than anticipated since the art shop lost it – my first ever painting after I'd dropped it off – but it was thankfully found in the nick of time. I dropped it off at the gallery with minutes to spare. I had a quick look at the other paintings. They looked great! In fact they looked like paintings that a "real" artist would paint and the artists I met clearly took it all so seriously. I really didn't mind if I made it to the final round. I didn't want to take a place from a talented artist who this kind of thing would actually be a big deal for. We were to be informed in about a month if we'd made the final selection.

I knew the procedure by now. The gallery would put up all of the final selections on their website at midday. If your number was not included in the grid it meant that you hadn't made it through. The morning arrived and, unlike before, I received no email. I didn't think much of that and waited patiently for midday. I have to admit, I was a little excited. Can you imagine! My first ever painting being exhibited at the Mall Galleries, literally opposite Buckingham Palace! That would be quite an achievement. The opening night would be a special opening and then the gallery would open the exhibition to the general public. All paintings would be for sale. I was excited but also realistic. I didn't feel like I deserved it or had put enough work in to merit the distinction above any other serious artist. However, I could dream.

At midday, the email arrived. It told us to go to the website. I quickly went over to the website and saw the grid of numbers. I could see in two seconds that my number wasn't included. I was disappointed, despite my expectations.

When I collected my painting I discovered that there had been over a thousand submitted, and of those only three hundred pre-selected and ninety chosen to be exhibited. I had beaten over seven hundred mostly professional painters with my first attempt. But what I remember most is that when I told them it was my first ever painting I was asked if I had Asperger's. When I asked why, he said because it wasn't normal to wake up and have these talents. Of course I laughed it off but the comment stayed with me. That night I Googled "Asperger's" and "painting". I came upon the work of Stephen Wiltshire. Stephen is autistic savant who was diagnosed with autism. His work is amazing! I knew of him from watching a documentary about him. In fact, I had watched every YouTube documentary on autism and Asperger's and savants.

So that night and the following day I read about Stephen and autism. I absorbed everything on Google. I slowly began to realise that, although I wasn't autistic, I related to many of the things I was reading. In fact, I thought it would be fun if I tried the Asperger's test. I found that one was used by medical professionals to assist with diagnosis. I actually found three. I decided to do all of them.

The main test, which was very long concluded, "You are very likely neurodiverse". I didn't understand what this actually meant. The second shorter test concluded that my high score showed "strong indicators of having ASD". The final test concluded that my score was below the "Median Score for people with Asperger's Syndrome", meaning that I was close to the cut off, which they described as, "You may have a severe form of Asperger's or other forms of autism."

I totally ignored these tests. I thought they were comedic! Me having ASD: that was "crazy".

My curiosity got the better of me though. Two things struck me. The more I read, the more I related to the symptoms, the more I realised that I had *so* many of the traits.

Bridge Boy

One of the tests asked the question: "Do you like bridges?" This struck me as very odd. The reason being that I love bridges and I love their architecture and design. I will always comment when seeing a new bridge. In fact, a friend even gave me the nickname "Bridge Boy" because of my obsession with bridges on every journey we took! So this made me wonder...

Poor face recognition

Another thing which interested me was that I was reading that some people with ASD or HFA sometimes had challenges with facial recognition of people that they know due to changes of environment and other factors. I'll give you an example. Myself and my then partner, Jacqui, went to watch a soccer game with a friend and his friend. I greeted my friend, Peter, and I introduced myself to his friend. He looked at me as if he had been insulted gravely! Peter, said, "Anthony, you know him from work." As I looked closer, it slowly dawned on me that he was a person that I had chatted with nearly every Tuesday for many years, but he was wearing different clothes – he wasn't wearing his dance clothes. I quickly apologised and told him that I wasn't wearing my glasses. This also confused me. I didn't have an answer for this. It dawned on me that I needed to take appropriate action now and get to the bottom of it.

NHS experts

The process of getting seen by an expert is long – sometimes months or even years. In fact, according to online sources, it seemed like the process meant having to convince the doctor of your symptoms before they would even consider sending you for assessment. I didn't have time to be messed around like that. I felt vulnerable and I wanted an answer quickly.

I decided to go private; with one of the best experts in the UK. He was pretty expensive but people were saying great things about him. I had to wait three weeks for my appointment and I was scared. I KNEW that I had ASD but I just needed the confirmation. I felt so alone. I knew I couldn't do this without a supportive partner and Jacqui was far from supportive. She had her own very complex issues as it turned out and that marked the end of that relationship.

Chapter 3

Advice on Dealing With Diagnosis

The time between discovering that I might have ASD and realising that I did have ASD was exactly four days. Those four days were probably some of the most confusing *roller coaster* days of my life. Shocking and bewildering. I also felt complete loneliness and if I'm honest, a little bit of fear and sadness. My feelings and perspective changed over those four days. At first I dealt with it with humour. Then it slowly dawned on me that this was real and that's when the real shock hit me. When I sat her down and told Jacqui she didn't understand, nor did she seem to care, making it more about her. I just hoped my friends would not have the same indifference as she did.

So, what do you next? You have ASD. Congratulations because this alone is an amazing step forward. You now know that you have the strength inside you to see reality and to see the truth about yourself. Many people do not have the reflective qualities and integrity to look within. There is a real fear with being potentially labelled as "autistic" – I get that, but if you battle on this can change your life for the better – bringing confidence, awareness and strength as well as some much needed solutions.

There is hope beyond the fear.

Fear is natural and you can eventually overcome it. It's natural that you will fear people's reactions. You might even fear that your family and friends won't believe you because you yourself don't quite belief it yet! You might think that your own mind is playing tricks on you and seeing things that aren't there. This is all completely normal.

Prepare

I wrote a list (based on my research) ten to twenty pages long of bullet points and emailed them to the expert before I saw him. I printed out copies to take with me. However, the most important part of compiling this document was the mental journey it took me on. I was looking back at my life with different eyes and writing down the results objectively. I felt sadness, despair, shock, surprise, regret and a wide range of emotions we have to go through. This package was essentially my life in written form and, with every bullet point being related to ASD, this contributed to resolving each one and my own personal self-development.

Grieve

I didn't have time to immediately grieve because within hours of my diagnosis I also had to deal with the end of my long-term relationship. So, I had to find somewhere to live in addition to processing this life changing information. It all happened so fast and when I look back, a lot of it was a blur. Consequently, it's hard to differentiate between what exactly was hurting inside of me. Ideally, you won't have your, what felt to me at the time, whole world as I knew it fall apart. But no matter what, you will probably be very emotional and upset. Embrace this! Cry and get it out! You are allowed and it's a really important thing to do. You must allow yourself time to grieve and to process your experiences in a new light. It's so shocking to realise that you saw the world and all your life experiences in a totally different way. That in itself is discombobulating and will take an emotional and physical toll on you. Allow yourself time to process and mourn the life you thought was real but are now discovering was slightly different to how you perceived it.

You will feel a range of emotions after diagnosis until you finally reach acceptance… and you will reach acceptance, I assure you. There will be a brighter day and the sun will rise in your life and it will rise higher and brighter than before because now you have clarity and an honest perspective of the world and your own limitations and you can work on those limitations and expand and improve. In fact, I believe strongly that "normal" people often do not ever take the opportunity to look within and change like we do, because we are FORCED to self-reflect, grow and change. Most people are too lazy to do this. There is no time limit to this. It might take a few days, it might take a few months or it might even take a few years. I was determined to deal with this full force so it took me a couple of months to work this out within myself but I firmly believe that it is a process, a never ending process of expansion, education and personal development. It can be exciting to improve every day, so it's a journey with no time limit that you can pick up at any time.

Regret

It is natural to look back with regrets and even feel shame. You will look back and consider the people you may have offended or hurt with deep sadness. What I will say is to consider this. Even in your deepest pain you are finding the time to look outwards and consider the feelings of others from the past, a past that you can't change and that in itself says a lot about you as a person. You have self-awareness and heart. That is a positive and amazing thing. Not everybody has this. You can still travel through the emotion of regret and shame but just remember to be kind to yourself and not be too harsh. The most important thing is that you change from this moment so that you do what you can do and nothing more or nothing less.

Forgive your old self who didn't know better and embrace the new self with your new discovery and never make the old mistakes again.

Peace

You will probably at some point also feel a sense of peace because you finally have an answer. If this peace is teamed with personal forgiveness and a sense of change, this can be extremely powerful and positive for you. You will feel mixed emotions but everything is valid, most are temporary emotions. Experience the good and the bad and get through them. You will, without doubt, become a better person if you can learn from these emotional responses and address them.

Anger

Anger is a normal emotion. Embrace it and process it. You might be resentful towards people from your past because, when you look back with renewed clarity, you realise that you may have been taken advantage of and wasted years on things you didn't realise and couldn't control. You will feel sadness that you didn't find out earlier. You may realise that people treated you as less than human or were rude to you. You may feel that you have to be better and have to work harder than "normal" people to get the same results as them. Do I need to remind you of the power within you? You have immense power inside of you to overcome. If you can embrace those emotions, and resolve them and move on you can use these emotions to energise your future. You cannot change one second of the past but you can learn from it. So, extract this value and use any emotional experience or sadness to that end. What can I extract that is of value from that experience and this emotion? This is the way you turn this into a personal victory.

Be angry! Then be intelligent!

After acknowledging feelings of disappointment, anger, sadness and negative emotion make sure you give the same respect to the positive strengths you have acquired too.

Mourn

There will come a point when the reality will set in that you are autistic. You won't now feel like you are "special" or "different" but that you are messed up and or at a disadvantage to other "normal" people. You may feel trapped. It's affected your whole life, probably adversely, and caused immense pain. It isn't going to disappear. These are legitimate. It's time to mourn and to be upset and expel those emotions and feelings as best as you can because there is nothing you can do, other than that, about those previous factors. You are allowed to be upset about this. It's normal.

Heal

Once the shock has passed you will soon realise that you CAN live because you've lived this far. However, this time you have a whole new perspective and advice and help. Finally a light shines in the darkness. Grasp it! It's time for positive change. Life is hard for everyone. This is your chance to change the script. Write it from this day forth in the most positive way you can for yourself! Do this for yourself! You got this far without knowing – you now KNOW! You can adjust now. You can make changes now. You can change the situation! It's time to heal and continue down a positive road. It will take a lot of hard work and it is a constant daily process. This is one of the joys of life. Mould your life like a project! You are the project manager.

The process of healing will ultimately, be a positive journey for you and worthwhile. If you ever need help for any unresolved issues in your life you should consult a medical expert who can help you.

Chapter 4

Benefits of Diagnosis by an Expert

There are some who say that it is not necessary to get an official diagnosis if you suspect you have ASD but I am here to encourage you otherwise. Of course, if you *really* feel that you don't need it and your life is enriched and you are happy, then I understand and totally respect that, but often confirmation comes as a blessing, it takes away the speculation.

While I did seek private medical help, if you are from the United Kingdom then you can get this free from the NHS, but it can take a while – however both routes are valid.

Self-diagnosis

I initially self-diagnosed. I also realised that I was not a medical professional and could be mistaken, which is why I chose to seek expert advice. There are many people who suggest self-diagnosis is a valid option but I would advocate a professional diagnosis because it eliminates uncertainty. If you do go down the road of self-diagnosis make sure you read as much as you can about ASD and communicate with the people that know you best and that you grew up with, if possible. They can help you identify traits and behaviours within you that you may not have noticed. This is a process of self-discovery and is worthwhile and valuable. As you progress you will have a gut feeling as to whether you have ASD or not. This may lead, even out of curiosity, to a professional diagnosis or to prove ourselves "correct" or even, in some cases, "wrong". Either way, any kind of diagnosis is not easy but will also often lead to a positive change in your life.

STEP BY STEP WHAT TO DO

Getting a Diagnosis – the Process and Some Practical Advice

ASD varies from person to person, so making a diagnosis can be challenging, especially when it comes to the high functioning aspects. A "diagnosis" or a formal identification of ASD can be made by a multi-disciplinary diagnostic team of medical experts. They sometimes will accept self-referrals, but in most cases you will need to be referred by your general practitioner or another medical expert you may be in contact with.

1) Book an appointment with your GP

It's important that you book the appointment only in relation to possible ASD. Don't mention it in passing, in relation to any other medical condition. You want an appointment to speak about ASD only so that it is looked at properly and not dismissed.

2) Convince your GP

You will need to convince your GP and show him why you believe that you have ASD – yes really – this is often the case. The best way to do this is to have prepared a list of all the things that have brought you to this conclusion. You should write everything down in clear, short and precise bullet points. This is for you to use as a prompt as well as making sure that you don't forget anything important. You will be nervous so if it's written down then it will help you. Also, the process of looking back at yourself and writing the list will help you understand the situation you are in better so that you can communicate your predicament to the GP more effectively.

Your GP will need to refer you to an expert for diagnosis so explain all of your issues and why you believe a diagnosis will help you. Be specific and give them lots of examples of challenging situations you have faced from social to sensory challenges and state that you want a formal diagnosis to be sure and confirm what you already feel. Explain how all of these things have affected your life. Some doctors will be really nice and understanding and others will be less so – be prepared for this! They're going to ask you some direct questions, like, "Why do you think you have ASD?" and it might be helpful to have the answers to these questions ready in advance. Be polite but be firm and insist on seeing someone with specific expertise in ASD for adults. This might be the hardest step but it will be worthwhile. Remember that most GPs are not experts who specialise in this but that once you have your referral you probably won't be dealing with your GP, in relation to this, again.

3) Take someone with you

When you visit the GP and any later expert after a referral, feel free to take a friend or family member for moral support. They can also double check that you are accurately representing yourself, in an often emotional situation. This way you will feel comfortable with the fact that you have been "yourself" with the doctors and they see the "real" side of you. Also, you won't worry later that you acted the "wrong" or "right" way. I wanted to go to the expert on my own but I had my friend meet me afterwards to talk it through.

On the other hand, you may want to be alone and get moral support later after you have had a chance to process the situation accurately. You certainly don't want dramatic people around.

4) Getting a referral and the assessment

The expert will often be a trained psychiatrist or clinical psychologist with experience in diagnosing ASD. You may also see a multi-disciplinary team for diagnosis. It depends on your area and location. They are often very busy so be prepared to wait for an appointment/assessment. I personally didn't have to wait to be referred because I went private, however, I did have to wait three weeks to see the expert because he was so busy. By the way, I looked my expert up and watched his videos online before I met him. I liked what I saw and heard and was completely at ease with him. I felt like I knew him due to my prior research. Even the best expert will have a challenge diagnosing ASD but they are trained to do so. The diagnosis itself will mean that they will talk with you and often ask questions but won't examine you medically or physically, so you don't have to worry about that.

5) They are the experts

The expert will ask lots of questions about your history and yourself and has techniques or 'diagnostic tools' available. I was so impressed by how quickly they get to the truth and see things that you don't notice. It will probably be a lot less stressful than you think and quite therapeutic! Let the expert do their thing and do whatever they ask. Answer everything thoughtfully and truthfully and leave it in their hands.

6) When will I find out if I have ASD or not?

My experience is seven to ten days. You get a full report with their assessment. It's often in medical language but it I found mine clear and understandable. In fact I saw the document as my new "bible" and something that I could use as an anchor point and foundation to start building a new life perspective. It's an amazing thing to have experts look at you and write down your challenges because you can use that to transform yourself for the better. Most people never even have this opportunity. The moment I read my report, my life changed. It also left me feeling "heavy". It took me a full twenty-four hours to settle but I realised that it was something special and an answer to a lifelong internal question and I was so grateful for it. It was in black and white and now removed any doubts.

Coming to terms with the results

You will probably have many questions after diagnosis with ASD but you will not necessarily get any kind of support. I received none. You may not feel the need for any. My expert advised me that I did not need therapy or counselling because I had done well enough to get to this stage, but suggested I continue on the same path of discovery. Even if that meant reading books and speaking with friends. This is especially the case with HFA. In other areas of the spectrum a formal diagnosis can mean access to certain benefits and services. I didn't feel the need for any of that kind of support anyway, but I did need a few supportive words. I couldn't really find very much when it came to books, so decided to write it myself! If you can afford it and need it, continue speaking with the experts. Research legitimate official websites and books and stay well away from certain negative blogs which are often not based upon fact.

Other benefits of diagnosis by an expert

It is not only you who will benefit from a diagnosis – your friend and family too. It will help them understand you better and adjust their behaviour to accommodate you. It will help them and help you to have a framework of medical facts. It will help them accept you and understand you more and also get rid of any doubts about other possible medical conditions.

Diagnosis can also be a comfort to the family unit as a whole, including yourself, because it will remove blame. You can begin the process of learning to make changes more adaptively.

Another very important reason for a diagnosis is to identify possible adjustments, adaptations and potential changes that may help you at work. You should not be disadvantaged in any way and accommodation should be made within the law. Diagnosis also improves self-awareness, self-enlightenment and helps identify certain personality traits that you can get to work on to improve yourself and the quality of your interaction socially and with the world.

But how do you best go about telling people?

Chapter 5

How to Tell People

As a follow-on from the previous chapter, I felt the need to show you how best to let those around you know of your diagnosis – because it's not always easy and you saw what happened to me.

There is a saying, "You can't unring the bell" and it means that once it's out, it's out. If I could go back in time I would do things differently. I hope you can learn from my mistakes. If you suspect that you have ASD then there is no real need to tell anybody, except your partner or parents and I'd suggest you keep it as quiet as possible until you know. Once your diagnosis has been confirmed it's very important to think objectively and consider the impact any disclosure might have. Within twenty-four hours of telling my partner, I was single again. If I would not have told her, we would not have broken up that day. However, that part I don't regret because if you really can't tell your partner because you fear them leaving you, then they are the wrong person for you.

When you find out about your diagnosis, you might feel excitement at finding an answer to a whole lifetime of confusion and questions. So, you'd think that the most obvious thing would be to tell everybody. Well, in theory, I wish this were true. However, you need to protect yourself at this vulnerable time. You'd expect people to be happy for you and non-judgemental and helpful, but the reality might be quite different. You need to first prepare yourself to be exposed to some disgraceful, hurtful and inappropriate comments. The world is full of wonderful people and it's also full of ignorant, evil and stupid people. You need to really think this through and do it in a controlled way which safeguards and respects your emotional wellbeing and works for your own advantage. This will be a very emotional time and you don't need to add potentially avoidable problems.

Realistically you need to accept that some people will be uncomfortable with the disclosure. This comes from within them. You may notice that they treat you differently. This can go both ways. For example, my work colleague and another individual I worked with treated me amazingly well! I saw the most positive way they changed towards me. They were more accommodating and sensitive towards me and it really helped me in a tough time. It's almost like they gave me a little bit more leeway and that really helped me. On the other hand, people may tell you to your face that it makes no difference but still alter their behaviour towards you. Some people will label you and you need to consider this before exposing yourself to it… you need to be ready!

Who to tell

I think you should tell who you want but just make sure you understand the consequences of doing so. Some people will tell everybody and others will only tell close friends and family. It depends on you.

You probably want to tell your close friends and family. I would suggest that you tell your immediate managerial colleagues because they might need to make adjustments in the work environment that can really benefit you. There is no need to tell your other colleagues right away because, what will you gain? Consider waiting for your emotions to settle down and then making an informed decision. There may be very real negative connotations and implications, from bullying to discrimination, so go slowly and consult with close friends and family. Ultimately, do what you feel is right and comfortable for you after considering the options carefully.

What to say

You could tell people directly with the words "I've been diagnosed with Autism Spectrum Disorder" or in any way you feel comfortable. Remember, that they probably won't know what it is so you might need to have a follow up explanation. Have something short prepared. Another thing is to be prepared to hear some crazy things. It will often start with "you don't have that" or "you don't look like you have it". Remember, that often they are just saying words without fully engaging their brains; they feel compelled to say something. It would often be better for them to say nothing but unfortunately that usually is not the case.

When to tell

If you are working in an official capacity, I suggest that you inform your employer as soon as you can. You might want to do so via an email. I think this is a great way because it cuts out any potential awkwardness and gives them time to consider the email and respond appropriately. It also gives you a chance to construct an email that you are comfortable with. Do not under any circumstances use Facebook or social media. It should be a face to face meeting or another way which emphasises the seriousness of the situation i.e. they should listen to what you are saying in a respectful manner and give you an appropriate thoughtful response. Another thing to consider is that you are protecting yourself by telling your employer in case of an incident down the line. It wouldn't be appropriate to tell them that way, so tell them in advance in the right way so that you can be sure that they understand and the message has got through.

Family members and friends may indeed not respond in a way that you anticipate. They might inadvertently be rude. Many were to me without realising it. Expect no apology because they "know not what they say", in the words of a very wise man.

Why I am telling and what to expect

Ultimately, this is such an important question. Think about this before you tell them. What are you expecting them to say? Do you want comfort? Do you want understanding? Do you want empathy? Do you want a change of behaviour? Do you want their acceptance? Do you want their support? Have you considered that you might not get these things? You can't force somebody to respond in a certain way. You must consider these questions because you will probably be let down by a lot of people who you'd not expected, unfortunately. This is the moment where you need to connect with your inner strength. It will be hard but it's easier if prepared.

Crazy reactions

When you can't see it on the outside, is it real? This is the way some people think, so expect odd reactions and insensitivity by some people. Some people just don't know how to act appropriately and in a respectful manner – it's got nothing to do with ASD or anything else.

Don't take it personally – just be prepared.

Positive reactions

When I told my friend, Nicky, she just listened. She was perfect. She said she would go home and educate herself about it. This was wonderful. No unnecessary words or foolishness. Simon, my best friend, just said that he was with me as did many others. Natasha works in schools and knew exactly what to say. Others said, "Thank you for trusting me with this". I'm so impressed by these people. It says a lot about them. I'm grateful to them. In the tough times you see who your real friends are and in my tough time, these people stood tall and it is my privilege to know them.

Chapter 6

Living with Asperger's

Sensitivity to Noise and Sound

- Personal Experience

From a very young age I've been sensitive to sound and noise. I'm acutely aware of particular frequencies, noises, banging, tapping, alarms – you name it. I am hyper aware. It sometimes causes me extreme discomfort. Before we look into how to address this issue, I'm first going to explain what I mean using real examples.

Cinema incident

I went to watch a James Bond film when I was a teenager. I was a big fan of the series, especially the older films.

As I sat down, I became aware of a high pitched noise. I looked around to see people's reactions. Nothing. It seemed to be only me who could hear it. The cinema wasn't particularly packed, as it was mid-afternoon. A few moments later the high pitched sound stopped. I remember feeling relief. It was only for about four seconds but it travelled right through my head.

Later the noise returned. As it travelled through my body and head, I knew there was no way I could enjoy the film. I looked around again and could see that nobody else had noticed it.

It was intermittent every ten to fifteen seconds. I looked up at the ceiling, sensing it was something to do with a piece of machinery or something in the film roll. Either way, I couldn't sit through it, I had to get out. I quickly left my seat and walked back to the lobby and asked to speak to a manager. I explained the noise and they told me that they would send an engineer to come and see me. I went back into the cinema. By now I'd missed so much of the film and was upset about that. However, my new mission was to find out what this noise was!

Shortly afterwards an engineer came to see me and asked in a very friendly manner, "What's this noise you're hearing?" I sat with him and explained, "There! Can you hear that! It's a high pitched white noise sound. It's stopped now!"

Ten seconds later, "There it is again! Can you hear it?"

He looked at me and said, "I can't hear anything".

"There it is again!" I said.

He looked at me and said, "Wait a minute, I think I might know what you're talking about." He was really kind; he was genuinely interested in identifying the problem and solving it. He wasn't one of those people who would just dismiss it because he didn't hear it the first time. He was an engineer so had that curiosity and problem solving attitude.

He looked at me and said, "This is very strange but I think you might be hearing the fire alarm batteries recharging. They automatically recharge every ten seconds and, I guess, they might emit a white noise or a very slight sound."

Straight away, I said, "Yes! That's it!" I was so relieved. He asked whether I wanted to sit and watch the movie and I explained that it was hurting my head and he invited me out of the auditorium and kindly gave me a full refund. I was really happy with the way he dealt with the situation. He looked at me and said, "Wow, you have really good hearing!"

At the time of course I didn't realise it was a symptom of ASD.

Hotels

What you might find strange, although maybe I never saw it as that at the time, is how I love to spend time alone. So much so that I would often book into hotels for a few days and then when I needed to change the scenery I simply moved to another hotel; sometimes just around the corner. For me that's quite normal.

So, on this particular day I checked into the Langham Hotel. It's a nice hotel in central London and quite elegant. I wouldn't put it up there with the Ritz or The Dorchester, but it's still pretty cool. As I entered the room, I was very impressed! It was even better than I expected. In those days, I used to love to sit and watch the news to relax.

After a few moments, I muted the television. "What's that noise?"

There was an annoying white noise coming from somewhere. I unplugged the telephone and the clock (as I always do when I'm in a hotel) and tried to identify the source. I suspected it was something to do with the fridge. I soon determined that it was too high pitched to be the fridge. I was also beginning to get a headache. As I was paying a lot of money, I decided I wanted to change room and relax without a high pitched noise blasting through my skull.

I went down to the reception and explained the noise and asked if I could change my room. They said that they would send somebody up to help. A staff member came and we had a chat about the noise but he couldn't hear it and couldn't help. I asked him if I could change rooms and he said I could, and took me to see two rooms. One was a room which I didn't like, which, ironically was more expensive than the room I was in. I gave that one a miss. The next room was a room which was basically identical. I thought I'd give it a try. I moved my belongings from my original room and settled into the new room.

I listened. The noise was there too!

I tried to tolerate it. I just couldn't. This time I wanted to get to the bottom of it. I was a little embarrassed to go back to the reception again, so I actually stayed in the hotel for a night and then went to the reception in the morning. After my investigation was complete. I had determined, in the middle of the night, that the speaker, near the entrance of the door, was emitting a white noise. Like an almost inaudible hiss. This time, armed with my investigation results, I went back to the reception and explained to the lady what the problem was. She looked at me like I was insane. I didn't mind. I just asked her to turn off the speaker in the room.

After a few phone calls, she explained to me that she wasn't able to turn off the speaker as it was permanently on for safety reasons. This upset me because I told her that I wasn't willing to have my stay permanently disrupted. As I spoke, a junior member of staff looked at me and said, "I know exactly what you're talking about. I've heard it before. You're not crazy."

Phew!

It was around midday and to be honest, my couple of days' break had already been disrupted enough, it was time to check out! I checked out and got a taxi, not too far away to Park Lane and The Dorchester Hotel.

As I walked in, I explained to the reception that I had had to check out of the Langham because my stay was interrupted by noise and I needed to be "saved". He looked at me said, "The Langham is a shit hole, welcome to The Dorchester!"

White noise and headaches

I not only experience the headaches inside; I also experience them just walking down the street. These particular ones were probably the most painful.

I used to live in Kensington, London, and every time I'd walk past Kensington Court Road I'd hear a high pitched noise. It was so painful to me. Again, it was intermittent; every ten seconds or so. I didn't find out exactly what it was but the last time I walked past, it was still emitting. I have deduced that it possibly a security measure protecting the nearby embassies.

Another high pitch noise was right in the middle of London's Leicester Square, next to the old Swiss building. This really hurt me, every time I'd walk past. I suspect that this is a high frequency designed to protect the area from pigeons. The idea is they can hear the noise but humans can't. It scares them, so they don't congregate in the area. But not only the pigeons could hear this one!

Apartments

I've moved out of at least three apartments in my life because of noise. My noise sensitivity really caused discomfort to such an extent that I had no choice. One guy would walk around, what seemed like twenty-four hours a day, right above my head, on wooden floors.

Another apartment had two girls who would walk around in high heels, constantly, above my head. And the funniest is how a neighbour chanted all night. Naturally I moved out!

Silent phones

Another thing which I've noticed is that over the years, my mobile phone has generally always been on silent. In fact, I choose to have a very old phone which doesn't have fancy applications. I've even got a second one which I keep so that when this one packs in, I can continue with the same phone that I've had for the last decade. I just like the familiarity and my philosophy which technology is that if it works, why change it?

I like to have that control and peace and quiet maintained and then when I notice the red light, I can choose to act and respond, in my own time and at my own pace. I have never missed a call or been affected by it. I just call back when I want, or more likely, I email back.

I don't really like phone calls. Phone calls, especially for mundane business detail. Those things can be resolved via email, in my opinion. I just like the idea of having that control and not having your life dictated to by a small piece of technology. I remember, when I got my first landline phone (which I needed for the internet connection), I disconnected it immediately. If I ever needed to use it, which was rare, I just plugged it back in.

Ambulances and sirens

If you live in London, you will know that one of the sounds you will hear very frequently is the sound of police and ambulance sirens. The emergency services are constantly on the move in London and you'll often hear sirens blazing through the night. I've always found myself reacting and getting upset by them. They hurt my head. Every time I hear one in the distance now, I cover my ears until it has passed and I am totally fine. I remember one of my first girlfriends, a beautiful girl, inside and out, Amalie, would sometimes cover my ears when she heard a siren. I don't remember ever talking to her about this or how she knew to do it. She is one of the two people who said, years ago, that she thought I was autistic.

Alarms and bangs

Alarms, bangs and unexpected sounds really upset me. In fact I'd go beyond the word "upset" to "they cause me physical pain". Amalie often had to wake up early and one morning her Lady Ga Ga alarm went off really early. I was so upset! As in, I was upset for the whole day. Another time, her iPod was playing really quietly in her bag. We were watching *Spooks* and I asked her what the noise was. She said that there was no noise.

I told her that music was playing from her bag. She went to check, no music was playing. It was really affecting me so I went over to the wall, thinking it was possibly from next door. Amalie's bag was on the floor and I hear the faint sound of Lady Ga Ga. It was her iPod on really quietly and I could hear it as clear as day!

I often move tables in restaurants if somebody has a loud, certain type of voice. I count the steps of the stompers in the museum. Even my best friend, and this really hurts my head, he loves to stomp. I asked him recently, "Why are you stomping your foot?" He didn't know what I was talking about. He did it again. I said, "There, why are you doing that?" It's a constant thing. People are not aware of what they do sometimes.

Musical tone

I also am very sensitive to musical keys and tones. I actually researched this because it at one stage it affected me so badly, it made me physically ill and nauseous. I'll explain. I was listening to the classical piece of music by Ravel, called 'Bolero'. It's a great piece of music. There is a part when a flute or a recorder comes in. As soon as I heard it, it hurt my head and I thought, "That's so badly off key!" I had to turn it off. How on earth could they let that get through on the recording?

The next day I researched the piece and the orchestra. There was no mention of it online. I looked up the review of this particular recording too and the same thing, nothing.

This surprised me but maybe it wasn't a famous enough recording. I took the recording to a musical friend of mine and asked him to listen and to point out whether in his opinion it was in key, or not. He said, in his opinion, it was. I knew that it wasn't. It was slightly off. A few months later, I pulled it out again to continue my investigations and I put it on. As soon as the flute section came on, the pain came so bad I thought was going to be sick.

One of my favourite artists is Nile Rogers of Chic. He is the real deal. I downloaded two of his songs, 'Le freak' and 'I want your love'. I have listened to these for many years but wanted new versions. Anyway, as I listen to the strings on 'Le freak', I noticed that the tape, which was probably the source for the recording had stretched. Consequently, it was very minutely off key, for a very quick moment. I noticed it straight away and told my partner. There are so many songs that I notice this for. I have a long list.

Later, I decided to purchase a new Nile Rodgers collection. It was a remastered version. I played 'Le Freak'. I knew it! They fixed the pitch stretch issue in the new version.

I also have the ability to identify the location of nearly any Michael Jackson concert just by listening to a snippet of the crowd. I don't have to listen to the music, just the crowd.

For fun, my friend, James, tested me out and he was blown away. I've always had that ability. It's nothing to me. I just know where the shows were performed because each audience has a particular unique aspect to it. Maybe someone has a whistle, or a girl screaming.

That same audience sound has even been used on other products since, including on his posthumous release, 'Behind The Mask' – that crowd and whistle have been annoying me for over twenty years!

(ii) Official Perspective

Often those on the spectrum are over or under-sensitive (or both) to sound. Certain sound and noise processing problems can have a major impact on one's life leading to headaches, pain, stress and anxiety. Often a person with ASD might not even realise what the problem is. What they have is in fact a sensory overload that is translated into irritation or possibly aggression (or "challenging" behaviour).

Hearing problems – Auditory Agnosia

Auditory agnosia manifests itself primarily in the inability to recognise or differentiate between sounds.

It is not a defect of the ear or hearing, but a neurological inability of the brain to process sound meaning. This can be particularly a challenge for those on the spectrum.

Meaning and decoding challenges

Some people on the spectrum have challenges with language which means that they sometimes can't understand and decode certain words and they might often just be interpreted as sounds. This is often the case when under pressure.

Tone

Others with ASD can have a problem with understanding and interpreting tone (musically or with the spoken word). Challenges including accurate decoding of inflection, subtlety, emphasis and, often, *implied* meaning. This means that subtext and undertone can be beyond the sophistication level of some on the spectrum and a challenge for others, who will often need clear, concise and direct language to act upon and understand.

Sound and noise overload

Many people on the spectrum have a major problem with filtering out sound which people not on the spectrum naturally filter out or can easily ignore. This means that a situation can be extremely painful for someone on the spectrum and totally fine for others in the vicinity without the same challenge. We are often overloading with different streams simultaneously and have awareness of them completely.

People on the spectrum can have an under-sensitivity or over-sensitivity to noise to such an extent that things can become muddled and sounds confused and distorted. Conversely we can often hear conversations from a distance and might have a problem switching off from that meaning that we can't concentrate on what we should be concentrating on or something that needs our immediate attention. This situation is often physically painful and very uncomfortable.

Or it can be reversed. For example, when I perform I need to have the music at an extremely high level – so that the backing dancers and band wear protective ear plugs. I need to feel and hear the music powerfully when I perform and I want it to drown out the audience. So, if I hear the audience (except when they are roaring or screaming) I do not like it. I use one type of sound to block out another.

(iii) Advice and Tips

1) Controlling your environment

As best as you can, take control of your home environment and create a safe space for recuperation and relaxation. Identify issues and solve them. If they cannot be resolved then move out. Direct tip: I once shared a house and the noise really affected me so I decided to hang lots of clothes on the door (noise was on the other side of the door) and then I purchased a sleeping bag… but not to sleep in, to place on the door when I was reading or working. This really worked as a sound barrier. It wasn't perfect, but it took the "edge" off the noise. On another occasion I really got upset with the noise on the other side of the bedroom wall so I got all of my products and books and "built" a wall. I then went to Camden and purchased a few strange eastern looking quilts and draped them over my "wall". This created a really good sound barrier, which didn't look too bad! I couldn't fully open the door, but I'd rather have that problem than the problem of dealing with noise.

2) The obvious things

If noise is a problem and it can't be resolved remove yourself from the situation. You are responsible for your own wellbeing so if you need to escape and move, do it!

3) Moving into a new place

This is an important one. If you are moving into a new apartment or property, take a look at the street before you even consider it. Is it a busy street with traffic? Are there restaurants nearby with possible extractor fans (cause smell AND sound). Without doubt the most important thing to look out for is the dreaded scaffolding! If there is scaffolding anywhere nearby the building, move on. Don't even risk it! Look at all of the buildings in the surrounding area, not just the front. Also, if you are moving into a shared building, try and go for a top floor apartment on the corner. These things might help because psychologically you will know that, at the very least, there will be no people above you and on at least two sides of you. If this is not possible then try your best to get as close to this as you can. Also, tell any landlords or estate agents that you have challenges with regards to this issue, in advance. This means that you will have a better chance or resolving, or moving out quickly, if noise becomes a problem.

4) Therapy

Try cognitive-behavioural or occupational therapy to resolve any psychological issues with regard to noise and sound which might be causing additional (beyond physiological) issues.

5) Painfully loud people in restaurants

Just move or walk away!

6) Covering your ears

Cover your ears when you anticipate fire engine and ambulance sirens – this really works! Also, interestingly, I find that people around me will copy me when I do this because it even hurts people's ears that are not on the spectrum too.

7) Earplugs

Earplugs are an option, especially at home or if you go to an entertainment or music venue.

8) Ask friends to pre-warn you

My best friend does this all the time! It is actually funny because he will inform me of the smallest sound he is going to make that doesn't even affect me! I see the funny side and actually really appreciate the consideration he shows. For example, he will say "I'm just about to turn on the blender" and then he will close the door. This kind of consideration is LIFE CHANGING, as a lot of the problem is surprise and the feeling of dealing with this on your own. When you know you are not alone and people care and are not out to hurt you, it helps.

9) Communication

Communication is key. People don't like to be told what to do or feel but if you give someone an opportunity to help, by explaining your condition and problem, they will often change their behaviour.

Chapter 7

Living with Asperger's

Sensitivity to Smell and Light

- Personal Experience

Smell

As well as being hypertensive to sounds, I am also sensitive to certain smells. In fact, I've always been aware of smells around me and they have quite often affected me.

I once entered a restaurant for my birthday in Covent Garden. As I sat down, I noticed that there was a strange smell. The smell itself was subtle but almost like rotting matter. I looked around and it didn't look like anybody else could smell it or were particularly affected by it. I continued to try and act normal and select my food but I couldn't get comfortable because of it. I looked around. I looked under the table, I looked to see if it could be anybody in particular. I even checked my shoes! My second guess was that the cleaners could be using a dirty mop. This is something which I can identify in ten seconds flat! I've never understood why somebody can "clean" a public space with a dirty mob and leave an obviously disgusting odour behind and not do anything about it.

On this occasion I was unsure at first but then I realised. It took me a few minutes but right behind my head was a vase with flowers in it. It looked beautiful but I took a smell and realised straight away – they hadn't changed the water enough and it stank. As I am sensitive I can identify what a "normal" person would not and I couldn't enjoy the experience until this was removed. I walked to the manager and explained that the water of the vase needed to be changed and that the odour was making it hard for me to enjoy my meal. He immediately removed it and as if by magic, the smell disappeared! My restaurant experience totally transformed. Small things like that are big things in my world. The fact that it was dealt with in such a friendly decisive way, also went a long way for me.

The plant pot one is actually a regular for me. I wouldn't exactly say that I go out of my way to work out how regularly the water is changed but I can usually tell very quickly.

Light

Another extreme sensitivity is to certain type of lights. It's not an issue with all types of light, but in certain situations. I'll give you a couple of examples. When I check into a hotel room, I immediately look at the light situation. This includes the clocks, the remote, the TV etc. I do my best to cover them up – especially digital clocks within television sets. At night they light up the room and this really disturbs me.

I will often cover up the lights with tape, which I bring with me specifically for this purpose. The only problem I sometimes come up against is that if the light on the television needs to be exposed so that it can be controlled remotely, and I cover it, it doesn't work. For this, I usually have a hat which covers it nicely.

Another thing I do is put a towel underneath the door. This is a good one for me because it stops the light coming in and it also has the additional function of being a slight sound insulation.

I've found that, generally speaking, the curtains in

most hotels are very good at blocking light, usually more so than domestic curtains. They sometimes have a blind and then, in addition, thick curtains. I really like this. However, if the curtains are not so thick, I don't particularly enjoy the light coming through the gaps and will do my best to rectify it and create some kind of barrier, with shoes or something like that, to hold the curtain in place to completely block the light.

It goes without saying that I unplug all of the phones and remove the batteries from the clock if it is a standard non-digital clock, as I don't like the constant "tick tock". Once I've done all of these things, I can then properly relax.

It's my understanding that I am not alone though. The owner of the Savoy Hotel in London, Prince Alwaleed Bin Talel asked that there be no lights in the royal suite. On his arrival, which was being filmed by an ITV documentary film crew about the relaunch of the hotel, the special butler was seen running to get tape and said that His Highness wanted ALL light to be removed. He didn't want to see a speck of light. They were to cover them all. I don't have a butler to do it for me currently, but I'm very happy to do it myself! It makes a big difference for me. I find that these moments in the hotels are times where I can relax.

Sarcophagus

When I lived in Kensington a few years back I used to tell my friends that I wanted to sleep in a sarcophagus! Have you seen those Egyptian sarcophagi? They look like gigantic stone bathtubs! Most of them have stone covers too but the ones that we see, in say the British Museum, don't have the lids. However, if you slept in one of those, you wouldn't hear any noise or see any residual light … you wouldn't be disturbed at all. Although you'd probably be dead! Carbon Dioxide poisoning would get you. However, the idea of being sealed from the noise and light appealed to me, at the time. My friends knew I was slightly "different" and I'm not sure if they were entirely sure whether I was joking or not, however, it got me thinking! What could I do to stop the constant barrage of noise and stimuli which was disrupting my life?

I decided that I was going to turn my apartment into a kind of sarcophagus but without the stone bathtub! First thing I did was to go to the art store and purchase very thick black cardboard and lots of thick tape. I then pulled up all of the blinds and covered all the windows. I mean ALL of the windows. I didn't want a single beam of light to enter. That seemed to work. I then got the cardboard and the tape and covered up every single light. I wanted complete darkness! I have to say, I did a pretty good job. However, you'd be surprised, you can never get complete darkness. The light somehow gets inside and I never worked out how. I presume that even though the light doesn't come through directly. It creates a kind of glow thought the card which we can sense and see. In addition I presume that the sun emits other frequencies and energy only in the day time, which we can sense. That said, it was pretty much pitch black and at night, it was completely so.

I then went to the shop and bought a couple of different types of earplugs to wear at night. This way I had created a kind of barrier between myself and the world. I lived like this for quite a quite a while. Maybe a year. I don't think my guests even noticed. But eventually I realised this was strange and soon afterwards I moved out of there.

Bathrooms

When I go to the bathroom, I often don't turn on the lights. Not only is this environmentally friendly (joke!) but it means that I don't have to adjust to the light. I can just "relax". My good friend, Colin, when visiting his home often says, "It does have a light that works, you know!" I would then turn it on, to seem a little normal. Another thing, on this particular occasion, is that the light is connected to a very loud extractor fan which stays on for a very long time. Talking about extractor fans. I'm not a fan of those, as you can probably imagine!

If I can get away with not turning on the lights, I will do so. If I'm rehearsing on my own, I will often turn off the lights of the dance studio. I remember, I was practising at a studio once for a show. I was teaching myself how to sing and I didn't want to be disturbed. I booked the studios for weeks in advance and every time I would enter, cover the window and turn off the lights and do my training. One of the ladies that worked there was a complete idiot; rude, mean and inconsiderate. I think all the staff hated her. Anyway, she would regularly open my, locked from the inside, door and walk in and say, "Oh, I'm sorry, I thought nobody was in here because the lights were off." I mean, if you are reading this and you're on the spectrum you will see the flaw in this foolish logic straight away and you will get it! I will say nothing else on that.

- **Official Perspective**

Smell is a big challenge for one third of people on the spectrum.

When we smell, the information goes right to the limbic area of the brain. The limbic system controls memories and emotions. Certain smells are hot wired to automatically trigger stress, fight or flight responses to warn against disease and other threats. Now imagine if the sensitivity level was turned to "high". This is why it is so powerful and overbearing for those on the spectrum. In fact it can be so overbearing that it results in actual physical illness such as nausea, gagging and vomiting.

Of course you can turn this sensitivity to your advantage. For example by spraying perfume that relaxes and comforts onto an item of clothing like a scarf, that can be used them in certain challenging situations. Certain smells will always make me sensitive to certain situations or remind me of people. This can be positive as well as negative. I was once challenged by the smell of a certain perfume of an individual which affected me adversely. I was in a situation where I couldn't get away and it was overpowering me. It was a perfume which I associated with a negative situation. I have a very accurate nose to such an extent that I once jointly won a wine tasting competition when I didn't even drink wine! I can recognise smells before others and this can cause problems for those on the spectrum because we can be preoccupied with a smell that others can't detect. This can also relate to eating, with relation to the environment and surroundings but also to the smell of the food itself.

Under-sensitivity to smell

As well as over-sensitivity, the converse can also be true. Some people have no sense of smell at all or a limited sense and this can cause problems like failing to notice extreme smells (sometimes including their own body odour).

Perception

Bright lights, certain types of fluorescent lights and even bright sunlight through a window can often cause distress, headaches and discomfort for those with ASD. This can cause behavioural changes as well as a variety of physical issues.

- Tips and Advice

1) Controlling your environment

As best as you can, take of control of your home environment and create a safe space for recuperation and relaxation. Identify issues and solve them. If they cannot be resolved then move out. You will probably quite easily be able to identify a problem because it will be obvious. However, if it isn't so obvious, then use your emotions as an indicator. Just sit and absorb and see how you feel. Eventually, you will identify what it is that is making you feel uncomfortable. The key is to identify and resolve – take responsibility for your own environment! You must control the things which ARE in your control.

2) Don't be afraid to change lights and experiment

Ask to have lights changed if need be. Communicate with your landlord/boss and attempt to resolve problems – any light issues within your own control should be identified and dealt with. This might involve changing a light bulb. If this is not possible, then you can purchase lamps that are more suited to you and use these instead of turning on certain lights.

3) Smell

Again, identifying the problem is the first thing to do and then the second is to work out how to solve it. This might need communication or, for example, if you are in a restaurant near the toilets, moving away. Ultimately, it might be moving away from the source of the smell permanently if you can't address it or remove it.

4) Learning to accept

Accept that you can't control everything in life and that external situations and habitats will never completely be as you would like and rationalise it with the fact that you can probably put up with more than you think. Tolerate some things outside your control but reward yourself later if done so with a humorous spirit. Communicate and talk with your friends and allies and make sure you recuperate and recharge.

5) Sunglasses

Embrace sunglasses! These are great to not only block sunlight and other types of light but also to hide behind. I once went to an airport and was sitting with friends in the restaurant and the staff member asked me why I wearing sunglasses – I was very close to making him feel very uncomfortable by saying something silly like, “I’m legally blind”, but chose not to. However, wear what you like which helps and if this means wearing sunglasses at night – do so! If people ask questions, tell them the truth! Tell them you have a “medical issue” or don’t reply at all. You don’t have to acknowledge rude questions or engage in any type of communication you don’t wish to.

Chapter 8

Living with Asperger's

Food and Clothes (Repetition and Routine)

- Personal Experience

The black outfit

It was the philosopher and mathematician, Pythagoras, who said, "Know thyself."

I am a creature of habit. I have worn the same outfit for fourteen years.

I don't mean that literally. I have different versions of the same outfit: a black polo neck top and black trousers, black shoes, black socks, black coat and sometimes a black hat. I also wear the same underwear, same T-shirts and the same socks. I often used to think of myself like 'BATMAN'. There is a scene in one of the movies where we see his bat suits in a row. I felt the same. I had lots of black polo tops and countless black

T-shirts. I just like them. I feel comfortable dressed like this. I have never been into fashion, so this way, I don't have to think too much about my clothes, I just wear what I think looks good. Over the years, I would often say, "If you're onto a winner, why change!" It's only when I was thinking about speaking with the ASD expert that I actually noticed this. I looked at a photo of myself from fourteen years ago and I was wearing exactly the same outfit as I was at that moment.

My friend, Moe, once persuaded me that I should change. I had never worn a piece of jewellery so we went to get a Swatch watch, brown shoes, various different colour jeans and different colour tops. Pinks and blues and browns. He also said that I should get a different colour coat, so I got a big grey one, instead of the usual black. He said that I looked great! I thought that it all looked pretty cool. I didn't feel particularly comfortable though. It just seemed like such an effort to coordinate and I didn't see the point. However, as I'd spent the money and wanted to make this positive change, I did it. In fact I wore the new clothes every day – changing the sequences of colour.

When I'd finished with one of the tops, I'd throw it into the laundry pile. It piled up until I had worn all of the new clothes. I didn't actually wash them. I just used them until they were dirty and then wore something else and repeated the cycle. When they were finished, I thought to myself, *time to go back to the tried and tested black*! And I did.

I feel this need to wear the same thing is more to do with comfort and routine. Sometimes, when I have run out of clothes, my best friend would let me wear a top or something. People would comment, "Anthony, you're not wearing black!" and I would reply, "Remember the rule, if it's not black, I've probably stolen it off my best friend!"

Ripping tags

Another thing which I have often done over the years, which I didn't think was significant, at the time, was to rip out the tags. They would often irritate me and make me itch. Often I'd rip out the tag with such force that it would leave a hole behind! I never cared about that though. As long as the tag was gone, I was happy. I didn't realise that this was also a symptom of ASD.

Food and the same meals

Similar to the clothes, I also have the same pattern when it comes to food. I have never had an issue with eating the same meal every day. In fact, if I liked the meal, I often enjoyed having the same meal every day! I never really thought about it, however, many times people around me would point it out and encourage me to eat something else, even though, I actually just wanted to eat what I wanted to eat.

For example, when I performed in Egypt we could eat anything we wanted and I knew what I wanted. It included a fresh mango juice, fries, some kind of meat steak and that was it! I ate this every day. They told me that it was good to experiment and try new things. Intellectually I totally understood and agreed with him, however, I still ate what I wanted!

Eating the same meal for a year

I'm sure there were some exceptions but I remember, looking back, in 2010 I ate the same meals, every day for one year, at least. It might have even been two years. I ate the same thing for breakfast. I would walk across the road and order my egg and bacon sandwich. Pick it up ten minutes later and eat it. I would then, in the evening go to the Chinese restaurant and get my duck and rice (yes, I put on a lot of weight in 2010!). Looking back, I ate this every day, without thinking about it. I also enjoyed it. It was stress free. I knew what I wanted and it was convenient.

Food is one of the most important things in life, but to me, it's just food. I don't feel the need to eat a different meal every day to enjoy it.

Routines

We all have patterns of behaviour. I notice that I alter mine according to the stresses and experiences of the day. It's almost as if I have an 'ideal day' set of behaviours and I have a 'stressful day' or more accurately a 'disturbed day' routine.

How I wake up

I find that the one thing that sets me up in the morning and will set the tone for the day, is the way that I wake up. After many years I have noticed that this affects my emotional state during the day. Ironically, it took me a very long time to notice this. If I awake naturally, I usually am very happy and neutral. I say neutral in a sense that I am not frustrated or disturbed and can then take a look at experiencing life from a balanced 'normal' position.

In this state I like to play piano music. I love the French composer, Erik Satie. For the past year it's been 'Trois Saraband'. Once that is playing I drink tea. Now I am ready to face the day.

But if I wake up badly… this affects me adversely and always has. It's not just a case of being grumpy. It's a case of being upset and frustrated all day and many times for more than one day – a few days. The number one culprit is loud noise.

It affects my ability to function in a normal way when abruptly awoken.

Framework of routine

The number one thing that disrupts and upsets me is noise. Over the years they have calmed down as I have come to understand myself. I like to prepare myself for going out in a certain way. Brush my teeth in a certain way, walk a certain route, sit down in certain seats in the metro. The train and metro one is almost exactly like an episode out of *Tales of the Unexpected* (a British television series which aired between 1979 and 1988). The wonderful author Roald Dahl wrote a short story called *Galloping Foxley*. He based it upon a true story. A contented commuter called Perkins travelled on the train every day. He was completely obsessed by punctuality and routine. He stood at exactly the same spot every day and got on the same carriage and sat on his favourite chair. Everybody knew their place and knew the routine and it worked well. One day a silver-haired strange looking man appeared in his spot! He then proceeded to sit in Perkins seat! This completely shattered his life, it would seem. Furious, Perkins then realised that the rude man who had taken "his" seat was in fact Bruce Foxley. Foxley used to be Perkins's prefect in school and treated him like a slave with constant bullying and sadistic behaviour. The story then recounts his childhood experiences. Finally, Perkins confronts Foxley and exposes him, in front of the well-to-do train passengers. Foxley then denies it is him and that Perkins has made some kind of mistake. A whole story unravels from this man's seat being taken and his morning routine being disturbed to the point of public breakdown!

This kind of story makes me smile. I can relate to it. I don't travel on the train very much now but when I did,

I felt personally insulted when somebody else had the audacity to take "my" seat. My seat, by the way, was the first carriage, near the door, by the window, left hand side. I then had a second preference on the opposite side and a third preference. It was unacceptable for me to sit on the "inside" and unthinkable that I could sit in the opposite direction of the train's direction of travel! The train also had to come on time, which was almost never. Oh, the joys of taking a simple train journey! If the metro is too full, I will often walk. I prefer to walk than be surrounded by strangers squashed up against me.

Music

One of the things which make me good at my job is my "obsession" with the same musical songs. However, the "obsession" is not limited to just my "work" music. I also repeatedly listen to certain jazz music, classical music and contemporary music. This familiarity with the music has helped me dance and perform over the years. I have listened to a certain song probably tens of thousands of times and taught the choreography thousands of times. I will also, when not teaching it, dance to it for fun and listen to it for fun, along with other music. I do not find this boring or strange. As I've stated earlier – I enjoy it, so why not listen to it! Many "normal" people would get bored by the repetition but not me, I actually enjoy it and feel like these pieces are like friends or family.

The band and work colleagues

When I perform I like to have the same people around me. I don't like change in that department. I want the same dancers to my left and to my right and behind me. I want the same keyboardist and drummer. I want the narrative to build and comfort and trust levels to grow. Consequently, I need the same people with me so that I feel comfortable.

Looking back, I notice that Marina, one of my wonderful backing dancers, has been on my right hand shoulder on every DVD project and nearly every show I have starred in – it just takes a lot of stress out of the situation.

We grew up together she knows what I like, she knows the dance moves that work, she knows when to leave me alone and let me focus on performing. When your team is like that and have been together for years, you can focus on your job which is to perform and put on an amazing show.

I think this is part of life generally of somebody with ASD. If your basic surroundings are stable and you can trust the people around you, you can then put all of your energy into dealing with external stressful factors of normal life.

The same goes for colleagues. At the dance studio one of the things which I love is the fact that the manager or the person that I deal with day to day is the same person. We have built up a relationship over a decade since his arrival and built up trust. I would feel uncomfortable if he was to leave and I have to rebuild a new relationship.

- **Official Perspective**

Clinical Psychologist Dr Elizabeth Shea claims why we have these habits and unusual sensitivities:

> *"Differences in the way the brain processes information are also documented in autism ... For example, cognitive rigidity and the 'desire for sameness' may result in an adherence to particular routines or rituals around food, such as having to have the same utensils, with the context being often the first predictor of whether a food is safe... may explain why these children*

> *notice the 'local' details of a food, such as a black mark on a crisp, at the expense of the 'global' or overall appearance of the food. This can also explain why foods are rejected if the packaging changes."*

Clothes can often be just as important as food for people on the spectrum. Colour, pattern and texture can affect sensitive people on the spectrum greatly. Many people on the spectrum don't follow fashion and will wear the same style clothes for years or what might appear to others, as "all the time".

- Advice and Tips

Food

1) Eat what you want (within reason)

Eat what your body needs. Don't stress too much about food or what other people say!

2) Eat consciously

If you're going to eat odd types of food or only particular types of food then you should look into its nutritional content. This, at the very least, is an intellectual exercise. It's useful to know how the food is grown, harvested and produced. This will help you in understanding what you consume and how it affects you.

3) Restaurants: eat where you are comfortable and happy.

Wherever you eat, at home or in public – be happy be comfortable. I once left three restaurants in a row because I was unhappy. Tell friends and family in advance of your sensitivities. Include them and request their help. Communicate your fears and challenges so this can be factored into choosing a restaurant. If you're going on a date or out with somebody new then use humour, in advance to inform them, like, "I just want you to know that I have strange eating habits but you can eat what you want and I want you to be comfortable."

People want to feel included and informed.

4) Be philosophical

Be philosophical about food and consumption. Know that if you really want to, you could change at any time so it's okay to break out of those habits sometimes.

Note: If you have serious challenges with food then you should seek medical advice. It is better to get help from an expert who is trained and can help with the specifics of your particular case. This is the case with all areas of life.

Clothes

1) Keep it simple

Clothes are an expression of who you are. And when it comes down to it, you can change your look at any time. Don't stress; keep it simple and functional. Your attitude and how you carry yourself is more important than anything you wear. I worked with an individual who had over £100 million pounds and he dressed exactly the same way I dressed at home, but messier. It doesn't, ultimately matter! But what you wear can make you feel good.

2) Vary the theme

As you know, I like to wear black and I love to wear black turtle neck sweaters but what also can work is varying the colour, so it's the same clothes but a little different.

3) Shopping

I hate shopping and I hate busy shops. When I shop I know what I want and walk in and walk out, rarely trying it on. This is totally fine. If you need to, shop online or ask a friend to shop for you. Do whatever works for you.

Chapter 9

Living with Asperger's

Hair and Hygiene Rituals

- **Personal Experience**

Personal hygiene can cause a lot of challenges and confusion for sufferers of ASD from not washing as often as they must, to compulsive cleanliness. When I wash, I don't labour the point, I will dash in and out of the shower; I certainly am not one for spending hours soaking in a bath. But I do have is a pre-set routine and I am a little obsessive about clean teeth!

One time it took a hair stylist to point out that my hair needed attention and made me realise that I did not even possess a hair brush!

What's interesting is that I never thought to brush my hair. It didn't even cross my mind. I just put my fingers through it and that was that! However, when I realised that maybe it wasn't normal to *not* brush my hair I changed my habits! How on earth could I not see that I needed to brush my hair?

I decided to write a list. I wrote a list of, drink water, brush my teeth and floss, hydro floss in the evening, wash hair, condition hair, have the shower, moisturise in the morning and then in the evening. It really helped. I started to do it. It helped more so when I was alone. When I went out to teach or work, I had a certain routine, so I was always clean. This might seem odd, but that's how it is for people with ASD; some things come less naturally.

- **Official Perspective**

ASD can also cause problems with personal hygiene and handling of hair amongst, other things. Some might mistakenly assume that this is an issue of laziness or dirtiness, however, this is often not the case as it is more to do with sensory issues and challenges as well as a lack of social awareness. In addition, younger people on the spectrum may not pick up on social cues or comments from peers in relation to hygiene, or disregard them, giving the impression that they don't care, which often compounds other social and interpersonal relationships. Consequently, young people on the spectrum may be more vulnerable to bullying than their neurotypical classmates. However, this issue can affect people of all ages.

I have challenges with controlling my stress levels when having my hair cut and especially whilst waiting. I understand that other people on the spectrum also find the waiting challenging, so this is not abnormal for people with ASD. I have less of an issue with the sensation of having my hair cut but this is often a challenge for those on the spectrum. From the temperature of the water, to the product used, to the physical proximity of the hairdresser – a wide variety to factors.

Some have no issue with not ironing clothes (I am a great one for this!) and if it looks fine then it's fine. If the hair looks a little messy then somebody on the spectrum might not really care too much about going out when somebody without ASD would feel ashamed to walk out on the street!

People of all ages on the spectrum might have other problems including:

Touch: As some are very sensitive the actual sensation of a shower might be challenging and uncomfortable, including having water on the skin. A bath would be quite out of the question for some on the spectrum due to the dirt as well as the perspective that it's a waste of time and water. Certain toothbrushes can hurt sensitive mouths and gums. Deodorant can feel awkward on the skin too and get over clothes and create a mess.

Sound: The sound of dripping water can cause distress. I have to make sure that the shower is off completely because I can often hear the dripping from another room and it gives me a headache. Other things like electric toothbrushes and razors can be challenging. I am affected by other people's toothbrushes (but not my own conveniently) and especially electric razors (which I don't use).

Smell: It can repel or it can compel. So, for example, those on the spectrum might only want to use one type of toothpaste and be upset if it is changed or not available and choose not to do it until the product they are used to is available. I will use, but not enjoy using toothpaste with little bits in and bicarbonate of soda. There is also a textual consideration related to touch and feeling.

Taste: This is often a problem for those on the spectrum and a challenge, so choose the right toothpaste!

- Advice and Tips

1) Make a list

Whenever I want to achieve anything I write it down and have it where you can see it every day. For example:

a) Wake up and turn left and drink a full glass of water
b) Go to the bathroom
c) Meditate for ten minutes
d) Brush teeth
e) Wash face and shower
f) Moisturise

This is a proven method. It needs to become a routine, like you are on autopilot. At this stage you can put the list aside or keep it to amend, it's up to you. If you have a special occasion, like a first date, for example, do a test run and ask a friend if you look and smell alright! Don't be afraid

2) The "drawer and bed" method

I read something online about a method to train children which involved putting products in one bucket when used and in another still to be used and it made me smile. I have a slightly different method which works well! I have all of my things in a special drawer (I don't like leaving them out or on the table because I drop them and knock them over) and then before I have a shower and get ready, I take them all out (everything I'm going to use) and place them on the bed. Actually, I'll tell you the truth… I sometimes place them on the floor! Then I systematically use the products and then after I've used them, I put them back in the drawer. So for example, the last thing out is usually the floss, which means that I have that to do – it helps keep track too!

3) Purchase products you like!

Experiment and test. I would also suggest that you keep it simple. Find what you like and keep an adequate supply!

4) Showers

If you hate showers I'll give you a top tip! Time it! Buy a timer and use it, this way you know exactly when to end it. Another secret technique I use it this… music! I know that when I have a shower, after starting a concert, it is time to come out before the fourth full song comes on and when a certain sound effect starts. I press play on the shows second song when I enter, let three of the songs play and then get out when it ends.

5) Hairdressers

If you visit the hairdresser then plan the time properly. Try to go when it's quiet and you won't have to wait. Communicate with them and explain why this is important. If you don't get on with the hairdresser or trust them, find one that you do and are comfortable with. In addition, if you really have problems then explore the possibility of the hairdresser coming to you.

6) Education and understanding YOU

Take the time to educate yourself and understand the benefits of all the things you do, including personal hygiene and then do it consciously. People on the spectrum are usually logical and intelligent, so it will motivate you. Understand the societal consequences of personal hygiene and presentation and then play the game – just because you don't like to do something, doesn't mean that you can't do it and incorporate it into your life successfully.

Chapter 10

Living with Asperger's

Fear of Doctors and Dentists

- **Personal Experience**

It's quite ironic that for over a decade growing up my best friend, Ryan, was a doctor. He went on to become a heart surgeon and then gave that up to become a CEO of a technology company. I actually visited the offices and held a morning motivational talk for his staff, recounting a story about how he and our friend, Moe, managed to get a top ten hit in the UK charts. It's a long story but a great one about faith and goals and believing in yourself. We achieved so much during those times. Myself, Ryan and Moe had a reunion dinner a few days ago after seven years. It was great to see them doing so well. Moe himself trained as a pharmacist. So, as it turned out, my two best friends were professional medical practitioners which meant that I was often to be found in a hospital or the pharmacy meeting them after work or working on some project or other. Consequently, I visited the Royal Free Hospital and especially Whitechapel Hospital regularly.

Now, this is ironic because although I would see the doctor most days he wasn't technically my doctor. If I had a problem, obviously, they would help me. Other than those guys I had an issue with doctors and dentists. It's funny, I never really thought about it too much. I only started to think about this when I thought that I might be on the spectrum and between that point and my official diagnosis. That's when I began to look back and notice some interesting things.

In the last thirteen or fourteen years I have been to the dentist once and never to the doctors. I'm perfectly healthy and very fit and I just don't like going. I had to visit the dentist a couple of years ago because I had to sort out a cracked tooth and at the same time I asked the hygienist to do a clean and check. They said that all was fine. The dentist himself was professional but the hygienist was bossy and I didn't like the way she made me feel. If I'd had the same doctor and dentist all my life and had built a rapport, maybe I would feel differently. I've moved so many times that you have to fill in all these forms and they ask you all these intrusive questions and then you have to go through the bother of sitting in the waiting room. Part of me is totally fine running the risk of going to the grave than having to go through all of that!

- **Official Perspective**

Many people with ASD find going to the dentist or doctors very stressful. Fear of the unknown is part of that. The "idea" of going is often, like many things, worse than the act itself.

Many times, the medical practitioners and their staff are not trained to deal with individuals with ASD or might not fully understand. This will compound the problem. Another issue is that an unexpected (or even anticipated) appointment will often be a departure from the usual day to day routine hence a cause of anxiety. This is because the usual safety net of familiarity and routine, which can be a calming framework, or the usual learned coping mechanisms, will be suspended to visit the doctors or dentists. In a way, it's an obvious "double trouble" situation because of the removal of familiarity and the insertion into this alien environment with people that are often not aware and can amplify the problem (which is quite ironic if you think about, because this is a visit to locations where you'd expect a full understanding of ASD!).

Once with the doctor or dentist, let's not forget that the patient with ASD must be examined, which can throw up another set of challenges because often the patient does not wish to be examined and is uncomfortable with people in their personal space, often uncomfortable being touched or even being asked to remove clothes that are special to them and help calm the patient.

When I think about visiting the doctors or dentists it's also the waiting that makes me the incredibly anxious. Then the fact that doctor's surgeries have "annoying" beeps, buzzers and sounds and an intercom system. There might be music playing and strange people doing strange things. Tapping and banging, coughing and babies crying. The coughing in particular is something that I can relate to as a potential problem for me. There are a lot of different factors involved and these are things which need to be interpreted, dealt with, and coped with in a public place. This can be very tough for some on the spectrum.

Other sensory challenges when actually with the doctor or dentists can be the certain type of fluorescent lighting and the equipment buzzing, including drills and other equipment. Even the small torchlight that they use and point in your mouth and eyes – if you have a particular sensitivity to light – can be a challenge. If you are distracted by these things it can make the whole experience harder for both yourself and the medical practitioner. If somebody on the spectrum has communication challenges then this could also be an issue, such as expressing pain when a dentist does something, or being extra sensitive to the slightest touch, which, ordinarily, they might not be, which, again, causes a wrong impression and can cause problems in identifying what the actual underlying problem might be.

It's my understanding that education in the medical community is improving. I read an information pack given to doctors which was brilliant. However, it's also important to remember that often doctors and dentists are overworked and stressed out themselves and might be more inclined to be accommodating to somebody extreme on the spectrum but not high functioning. I feel this is a fair point because if a doctor or dentist is meeting you for the first time, a large part of the dynamic will be first impressions. Communication in a very short limited amount of time and sometimes if you look good and communicate well then you might not get the same accommodations as somebody who doesn't communicate quite like yourself. On the surface you are calm and might look wonderful but under the water, the feet are treading water overtime!

- **Tips and Advice**

1) Rehearse

When we perform we rehearse so when the lights, music and the audience start screaming, we are not surprised and know exactly what to do because we have done it many times before. It's familiar to us, which means that even with the additional factors and stimuli we can still perform because our bodies are on autopilot. We can apply the same principle to visiting the dentist or doctor. Rehearse the visit in advance! Don't be afraid to visit the surgery and take a look around before you visit. Sit down in the waiting room for a few moments. Familiarise yourself with the staff and feel free to explain what you are doing if they ask. It's also a good idea to have a walk around the local area or have a drink nearby too. If it is far away then read about the location online and use Google Maps and street view. If you are a young person or a carer for somebody on the spectrum it might even be an option to rehearse with chairs and play out a proper role play. Do whatever you need to do to make life comfortable and the experience as easy as it can be.

2) Plan

It's very important that once your visit is confirmed that you plan the logistics carefully. Think of it like you are a VIP or the President of the United States is arriving – protocol and planning is key, except this time YOU are the VIP! If possible contact the clinic and find out when the quietest time will be and visit when the likelihood is that there won't be a lot of people in the waiting room or nearby. You might even be able to book an appointment at the end of the day when everybody else has left, or the earliest appointment before people arrive. Timing is key and they might even appreciate it if you come in when it is quiet as it's more convenient for them. You do not want to be queueing or spending unnecessary time in an uncomfortable unfamiliar waiting room environment, so do all that you can to avoid this by communicating with the practice in advance.

3) Communicate

When you're planning your visit make sure that you tell the practice about any concerns and fears that you have in advance. Most of the time they will be happy to accommodate you and help allay them. Remember that, although they might not be perfect, they are trained professionals and have seen every embarrassing serious illness and problem under the sun. Tell them your problems! As long as you are polite, friendly and genuine they will be happy to help you and go 'the extra mile'. When you realise that they are on your side and accommodating then that fact alone will help you relax. Communication is important and communication in advance is even better because you'll be more likely to be in a better state of mind. Don't leave it until you arrive to address potential issues.

4) Rationalise

Understand that in life, at times, we must all go to the dentist and the doctor. Educate yourself and understand the reasons and the benefits of going. This will help the process significantly. Know that this does not have to be a regular thing and that it might be once or twice a year. Convince yourself with facts and acknowledge the benefits of going even though you don't like it. You will realise that you spend a lot of time doing things that you don't like and that sometimes just getting them done quickly and efficiently is the best way. Complete the task and move on to what you do enjoy!

5) Involve

Have a friend or family member help you with the planning and logistics. My friend is not very good at talking on the phone to often seemingly insensitive call centres and receptionists and arranging these things and I have called on his behalf many times. It can save a lot emotional stress and energy that you can use for dealing with the actual visit. Feel free to enlist help! Many times people will be happy to help you. You don't have to do this on your own necessarily!

6) State of mind

On the day of the visit make sure that you are in a good state of mind, as best as you can. Everything that is in your control make sure is as you like it. Eat well, sleep well, relax, recuperate, exercise, listen to music – do whatever it is that you need to do to be happy and strong! These things aren't nice at the best of times for people that aren't on the spectrum so you are not alone and it's a big achievement to go through this with our challenges. Arrange in advance a really nice reward after the appointment or later on in the day too! This will give you some motivation and make things flow a little nicer.

7) Music

If you like listening to music then ask permission and take along your personal stereo. Make sure that you tell the practitioner or receptionist, so that you can hear when you are called. The doctor or dentist may even let you listen to music whilst in a procedure! I once sat in and witnessed a plastic surgery procedure whilst the person received an injection whilst listening to a song on full blast with a personal stereo! He needed it to help him through and it worked! Take whatever you need to be comfortable. If that is a cushion, take your special cushion. If that means you want to take a friend, take a friend! I'd suggest that you keep the medical practitioner aware though and if you are too shy or embarrassed to tell them, have someone else do it for you. People want to be included and they will often be privileged that you are letting them into your world!

8) Compatibility

If for any reason you feel that you can't interact with a certain medical practitioner then you should make contact with their receptionist and communicate your doubts and fears. If you have been upset and feel that you can't get over it, you should find a new medical practitioner and make any necessary official complaints. Not everybody is compatible, so if you need to move on and find someone more suitable for you, then that is sometimes a valid option. I would suggest that you make this decision in collaboration with others, including friends and family or peers.

Chapter 11

Living with Asperger's

Forming Relationships

- **Personal Experience**

When I use the word "relationships" I am not only talking about romantic ones. I am talking about all type of social interactions. Anybody on the spectrum will inevitably have issues with this.

The key is to learn, grow and to experience life to its fullest. Be the best that you can be and have the best relationships that you can. If you try your hardest is this department you will be just fine. In this chapter, I'm going to talk about romantic relationships, i.e. girlfriends and partners and then later on we can take a look at some lessons we can learn from some of my experiences. I'm just going to give an overview of some things that might help others improve their relationships.

Being in a romantic relationship can be one of the most magical amazing experiences that we as humans can have. On the other hand, it can be pretty hellish if paired with the wrong person. If you are on the spectrum and have found yourself having relationship problems – do not fear – you are not alone! The key is to learn and to not make the same mistakes again.

Loneliness is a big problem for some of us on the spectrum. Have faith, my friend, and work on understanding yourself and being the best person you can be and I guarantee you, magic will happen in your life and you will have your wish. I'll tell you a story …

My partners

I've had a few serious relationships in my life. All of my partners have been extremely beautiful physically. One was and still is a famous actress who starred in some of the biggest movies of all time. In fact, let's say top five movies off all time. Let's call her "Evelyn". Another partner was called "Amalie". Amalie was and is a dancer and is an amazing person.

You've already been introduced to "Jacqui" and finally, "Eirin" who wasn't a very nice person. In fact Jacqui and Eirin both had a lot of similarities. My relationship with "Eirin" didn't last long because at first I thought she was just pretending to be a horrible person, I thought it was all an act… then it became clear, that no, she was just a pretty horrible person for real!

So what of Evelyn and Amalie? I have to say that from the bottom of my heart I will always love them both and cherish my time with them. Ironically Evelyn, a worldwide star, and Amalie, a very successful dancer, both stunningly beautiful are and were extremely loving, caring, kind and classy girls. They were often the centre of attention but did not court it – they were just naturals. In fact they were a little bit shy.

The first time I saw Evelyn I was taken back by her aura and magical quality. There was something about her. She was shy and beautiful. When I started dating her I just copied what I saw in the movies. Before we got too intimate I decided that it would be proper of me to go and meet her mum and dad and ask them permission to be in a relationship with their daughter. The first thing I did was email her mother. Her mother replied that she was very happy and had heard all about me. We were off to a good start.

My first proper Christmas

I had spent the last six or seven Christmases on my own and I think I was overwhelmed to be invited to spend this one with Evelyn and her family. I felt like an alien and didn't know what to do – even though they were so kind. It was too much for me.

Over time, we drifted apart. I know that it was probably my fault. Emotionally I think that I switched off. I wasn't sophisticated in the relationship department and sometimes I felt like I just went into an "emotional standby mode". I explain this as I still feel emotion but I almost lose the ability to communicate it. It must have come across so cold and I deeply regret any pain I caused by being emotionally distant. Even though I wasn't connecting emotionally I still always loved and was attracted to her, even if I wasn't able to show it. I've learned a lot about myself since this and cherish the moments with her.

I learned a lot from my relationship with Evelyn. By the time I met Amalie I was a little bit more experienced but still naive when it came to relationships. If I could go back in time and experience this again, I would do it all differently. I was cold, I was very much on "emotional standby" way too much and she still loved me and treated me so kindly.

It was like there was a block emotionally. I remember trying to work it out whilst being with her. Since, I have worked it out. Amalie is and was so stunningly beautiful. On our first date we walked all through the night for hours around London. Any girl that will walk around with me is a cool date! I loved that about her because that means I could feel free.

Amalie was also quite shy. You'd have never have believed it. Male friends would come up to me and say, "Anthony, that's it then right, you're going to marry her and be done, right?" Something was wrong within me. I couldn't connect emotionally with that. It was like I was scared. I remember she travelled to Germany for a while for work and internally, I just said, "That's it, end of relationship." I felt abandoned. I didn't even respond to her messages. I deeply regret this. One time, she came back and surprised me on my birthday and I hated it. It was the strangest thing. I remember it like it was yesterday. My best friend planned it with her. He took me to a restaurant and she arrived later.

I wasn't happy about that because I didn't understand what was going on. If they would have prepared me a little I think it would have been better. Anyway, when Amalie walked in my first reaction, wasn't "Oh wow, that's Amalie!" My first reaction was, "What a coincidence that Amalie has walked into the same restaurant that I'm sitting in."

I didn't even realise that it was planned! My best friend explained. Again, I wish I could go back in time and hug her and thank her for coming but at the time, in the middle of it, I was confused and shocked.

We are in contact now but I met her again a few years later. I apologised to her for everything and thanked her for being so nice. When I was diagnosed with ASD I messaged her and she said, "Anthony, I always told you that you were autistic!"

- **Official Perspective**

Many on the spectrum are perceived as loners by choice and live in a solitary almost monastic way. Even though this might be the case for some, for many this is not the case.

It's pretty obvious that to interact successfully with people we need to have been trained and taught appropriately through upbringing and in addition have the ability to learn. The challenge is that, in addition to perception and communication problems, people on the spectrum often miss out on this because they are too busy prioritising *survival.* Many times, also being subjected to bullying, rejection and ridicule.

Already finding it challenging to understand what others think or feel they are significantly disadvantaged, often, by adulthood they can be traumatised by past experiences and mistakes, challenged with understanding and communicating affection and love which can cause major problems later with finding a partner and achieving a long-term successful relationship.

People on the spectrum might also have issues with expressing emotions and understanding what love is and how to experience and express it. However, Plato himself said that "Love is a serious mental disease", so it might be the case that none of us understand love but that people on the spectrum have a challenge doing the things that people expect of them. It can be confusing for most people but a gigantic mountain to climb for autistic people. Typical and obvious displays of affection are not obvious to many with autism which means that this can cause friction in a relationship and confusion. A hug might be perceived as a threat when it is in fact a display of affection and love to a person with ASD. The instinctive reaction to that gesture might be perceived as a rejection or an insult by the partner leading to more confusion and bewilderment, when it is nothing of the sort. In addition to this, if a person hasn't practised how to act or been taught how to be in a relationship they may turn to Hollywood or television and copy that leading to calamitous results!

Development and escalation of relationships

Understanding and interpreting the subtle cues and flirting involved in a partner wanting to change the stage of relationship (say from dating to serious romantic relationship/partner) are often skills that are not intuitive for people with ASD. This can be extremely confusing and frustrating for both parties and seen as a sign of rejection when it is nothing of the sort. I myself find this really hard, so my solution historically has been to err on the side of caution and a girl would have smack me in the head and be super direct to get me to understand that they liked me in a romantic way. I have to hear it in a direct undeniable way otherwise I have doubt and don't know where I stand because my skills aren't as tuned as others not on the spectrum. The irony is that they might take this as rejection when it's actually extreme consideration for them in a confusing situation. One of the difficulties for people on the spectrum is that it can be tough for us to interpret someone's intentions, so they often would need to be direct to make a point, otherwise it might get lost, ironically in politeness. The individual on the spectrum might really want that affection and want to know that a lover feels that way but they can't see it and it "goes over their head". We often can't always read romantic signals that are "blatant" but still not direct, in your mind.

Another consideration is that we are often not as experienced in relationships and take a longer time to learn things as we've probably started being concerned about relationships and romance later. I had my first girlfriend very late, after my teens, when many of my peers had their first relationship within their teens.

Recuperating

After dates and social interaction somebody on the spectrum can feel exhausted by having to try and understand and interpret body language and all without the usual social skills. However, this doesn't mean that they don't want to go out or date, it just means that they might need certain environments to flourish better, or with certain types of people and then have recuperation time afterwards. I wish my partner would have given me recuperation time. When we went out I often had a great time with her but when I came back I often wanted to spend a little time alone. She would never give me that time, as this was perceived as rejection and this would cause me discomfort, which was totally unnecessary.

Thirty minutes' recuperation and I would have been able to give her more attention and affection but the empathy and understanding just wasn't there. I knew that I couldn't even request recuperation time, as the couple of times that I had – fire and destruction would come my way, then, or later!

Expressing Love

People on the spectrum might be considered bad at expressing love and affection. I would add that this is in the CONVENTIONAL way. We often express it in other ways too and if we learn what we must do, or are simply asked, we can do the other things too. My partner once confronted me with such anger – her face was contorted – because she said that I never put "kisses" and "hearts" in my SMS messages and she did it all the time. I just saw them as immature and pointless and not an expression of love at all. I might be on the spectrum but I can tell you now that love is NOT that. It might have been to her and that is part of why we didn't last together. I understand that many of us on the spectrum are not so good at expressing what is on the inside and can shut down at important moments when our partners need feedback or an emotional reaction. This must be tough for them if they aren't educated in what to do or have an understanding of autism and the behaviour of people on the spectrum.

Great in relationships too

People on the spectrum are often not involved in manipulation, are loyal, are honest and this can even help in a work environment and not just romantic relationships. A pioneering company in Denmark gave people with autism a chance to apply their skills to jobs from IT to product testing, reported a UK newspaper with the headline: "Better, faster… and no office politics: the company with the autistic specialists". Office politics and cheating are not behaviours often attributed to those on the spectrum. If they are in a relationship with you, you can probably feel secure in the fact that the amount of energy and effort it might take to meet somebody else to even be in a position to cheat would probably not be anywhere near worth the stress and hassle!

Being perceived as aloof and standoffish

If I got a dollar for every time I have been told, in my life, "At first I thought you were rude but you're actually really nice" I would be a billionaire for sure! This has happened all my life. I certainly must look a certain way because I am perceived in a way which is very different to my real personality.

Big Bang Theory

There is a very famous TV show called *The Big Bang Theory*. I don't watch it. In fact I don't watch much TV but on one occasion, I did watch *The Big Bang Theory*. It's my understanding that the protagonist is a high functioning autistic or somewhere on the spectrum. I thought that the actor was brilliant and the show was fine. One thing that is interesting though is that my best friend said to me that I was like the main character.

This was before my discovery.

Generally, I am aware that I am known as standoffish and aloof. Less so now but for many years, this was the case. I rationalise it quite easily by knowing that they don't actually know me at all.

The people who know me, get to know the more "real" me and I take their perspective more seriously.

When I teach I have a loud voice, mega loud actually, but I never used to speak with anyone or make eye contact or speak loudly – I have trained myself to do this over the years and am very good now. However, I used to be terrible!

Social imagination

"Social imagination" is the idea that we can imagine and "predict" what others are often thinking and the way that they will or may behave in a certain situation or to certain stimuli (i.e. words and actions). Another way of thinking about this is the idea of "flexible thinking". People on the spectrum often have a strict routine or set of behaviours. They may walk a certain route home. They might find changes to this challenging. The unfamiliarity can course distress. Consequently, this may affect the ability to predict a certain usual comfortable outcome which is usually expected and thus cause problems. This difficulty in predicting accurately what might happen when a factor or factors, people, circumstances or situations change can cause what is often perceived as "aloofness" or "standoffishness".

Social imagination, understanding challenges might mean that people on the spectrum may find it hard to:

1. Cope with meeting new people or in new unfamiliar habitats and surroundings.

2. Have challenges putting themselves in other people's shoes, at times and imagining the world from someone else's perspective.

3. Might find it challenging to work out that other people may have different thoughts, feelings and perspectives to theirs.

4. Find it hard to interpret others thoughts, feelings, actions, intentions and motivations.

5. Predict outcomes that others see as "obvious" or inevitable.

6. Prepare for change and various alternative outcomes.

Consequently, all of these challenges can add up to being perceived as aloof and standoffish. However, as these are only subjective opinions.

Withdrawal

Some of us with ASD can be perceived as being "loners" or "recluses". While this may be true – it is not always the case. It gets complicated because these behavioural patterns of being detached from other people and social relationships, choosing activities to do on their own or without people around are common traits in ASD sufferers. Some people do actively seek out and prefer these types of situations to social ones, which gives an impression of "coldness" compounded by the fact that somebody on the spectrum is indeed happy to be alone compared to a scary social environment. All of this adds to the "aloof" and "standoffish" label and perception. It can cause problems at work, in the office and especially in personal and romantic relationships.

The trouble is not that people with ASD often experience problems in expressing internal feelings and emotions, such as through facial expressions or through speaking. This compounds the challenge because we can't often then perceive the situation accurately, leading to us closing down and the situation spiralling to isolation and intentional withdrawal to try and ease the discomfort and pain. When a partner or friend tries to comfort or interject, it might even cause more problems because then the security blanket that has been created by withdrawal is violated causing more stress and discomfort. This can propagate into a vicious cycle and, instead of understanding it, it's easy for some people to just say, "That person is rude and standoffish." However, there is much more than meets the eye going on here.

- Tips and Advice

When engaging in relationships of any kind we want to have a sort of compatibility, which means that we want to be able to function and work together. However, if you think about, how many relationships actually function efficiently? Well, I've just had a look at the marriage and divorce statistics in the UK and I'm actually a little shocked. It shows that in 2012 there were 262,240 marriages, which was good you'd think, right? Wrong! In the same year, there were 118,140 divorces! That is an absolute tragedy! The point is that people, generally don't have basic compatibility that often. The failure rate is disgraceful.

I have tried to look at the statistics for marriages where one of the partners has ASD but there is nothing conclusive and, either way, 50% failure rate is terrible, ASD or not – so let's just look at it as it is. We, collectively, are pretty rubbish when it comes to compatibility and marriage (overall).

One interesting opportunity for a relationship where one has ASD is the opportunity for self-reflection. People on the spectrum often ask themselves more questions and have an understanding of the way they think than people not on the spectrum in my opinion. This means that there may be an opportunity to cultivate compatibility and understand using ASD as a vehicle. Any relationship is a challenge and as ASD relationship is no different! I believe that if we choose our partners more wisely, we can increase the likelihood of successful relationships. There are always exceptions, but these are my thoughts from my personal life experience.

In life there are always exceptions so take these as they are, just my thoughts, based on my personal experience:

1) Compatibility

If you are on the spectrum and would ideally like to be with a partner, if you choose to be in a relationship, who has a) Intelligence to understand what ASD is b) Empathy to stand back and appreciate how it is for you. c) Kindness – Guiding and Loving to help with the challenges of day to day living. d) Stable, Secure and Strong enough to be your rock. Insecure people can often exacerbate problems. e) Mature and Grounded in Reality – you don't need someone with their own complex dramas. Don't use your brain power to decode the manipulation, communication and personality problems of others! f) Principled, Loyal, Honest – this is self-explanatory. People on the spectrum aren't usually sophisticated and manipulative. I found that I had no chance of interacting with seasoned experts of manipulation and dishonesty. g) Patient, Insightful, Non-reactive – they need to know what to do and know not to exacerbate the problem, let it calm down and analyse and resolve later. They can't be explosive and reactive because it just doesn't work. h) Forgiving: you don't need someone who holds grudges. You need to build trust by letting things go.

2) Don't take any nonsense – red flags!

Acknowledge and make a determination about ALL potential red flags from DAY 1! Use Google, use your friends and get advice. Make a determination early on and if the red flags are major enough, end the relationship or tone it down until trust has been built. Have respect in yourself and don't ignore warning signs because you think you can't get better!

3) Better to be alone and try and be happy than with a dysfunctional destructive person!

You CAN be happy without a partner! So work on yourself and be happy and then you will be more likely to meet a partner who is closer to where you are. Better to wait and enter a healthy relationship with somebody who is compatible.

4) Start with friends and build from there. Don't jump right in.

If you're new to relationships, start slowly with friendships and then build slowly over time. This is the safest way and this way you will have a stronger relationship. It takes time to understand each other and takes time to understand ASD – invest the time and you will reap the rewards later.

5) To achieve a successful relationship, a person also needs to understand and respect themselves

Ask yourself whether you honestly respect and understand yourself. If the answer is "no", try to resolve this within you before aiming for a relationship.

6) Official diagnosis can make a difference in your relationship

Official diagnosis can help your partner better understand, acknowledge and face certain difficulties. There might be an element of denial so if it comes from an expert, then that will help them rationalise it, especially if they feel that they have experienced hurtful or indifferent behaviour.

7) Communication and acceptance

Once you have an official diagnosis you need to communicate with your partner and make a plan of action. I attempted to show websites and videos describing the condition to my partner at the time but I realised that she had already made up her mind about the condition and no matter what I told her or showed her, she wouldn't accept it. Both parties should have a good understanding of ASD and how relationships are affected by it. It's important that both partners make a serious commitment to making the relationship work.

8) Take the initiative and self-advocate

It's important that you know your boundaries concerning what is acceptable and unacceptable and communicating them, in a polite and respectful way to your friends and peers. Remember that, generally speaking, people will respect you if you speak clearly and honestly. If you find it hard to do this face to face, you can even email or write a polite note. However, verbal communication often works better.

10) Psychotherapy

Psychotherapy is a form of treatment which can focus on increasing general coping mechanisms, improving social interaction, wellbeing, communication and self-esteem. They can help look at your life and help understand better your compulsions and personality. This can be very helpful. The more information you have about anything, including yourself, the better you can address challenges and issues and possibly identify a solution. Another good thing about psychotherapy is that you can speak with an expert who can give you a summary of his thoughts in writing.

11) Trusted friends are your guardians

Don't ever forget that your trusted friends are also your guardians and helpers. They are on your side. They are a valuable resource and help – don't let these wonderful people and their insights go to waste! Vice Versa – you can help them too, maybe in other ways.

12) Make it a habit to listen more

Be the light and a good friend to somebody else! Make it a habit to learn to listen and listen for real! Be valuable to your friends and people that you know. This way, they will appreciate you and help you and you will feel rewarded and valued.

13) Being in a relationship

Being in a relationship with an ASD is hard at times because ALL relationships are hard. Bear this in mind and give your partner a break sometimes. Educate yourself on being empathetic. Remember that if you are on the spectrum you might very well have challenges with perception, which means that you might be able to learn from your partner's criticisms because they might be right!

14) Partners with unresolved childhood trauma or abuse unwilling to address them

The late veteran family therapist, Peter K. Gerlach, MSW said something that I totally relate to. He suggests that individuals with unresolved childhood trauma or abuse have a very tough time building a healthy relationship with other people with unresolved childhood trauma and abuse. He suggests that if both partners are willing to address issues then a successful relationship is possible, however, if only one is willing to address themselves and not the other, than there is a very large chance of almost certain breakdown and destructive behaviour in the relationship. Consequently, I suggest that you pick a partner who is healthy for you who you can work together with in the spirit of truth and honestly. If your partner doesn't accept their faults and challenges and express some desire to change and resolve them, then you should consider whether that person is right for you.

Chapter 12

Living with Asperger's

Coping with Loneliness

- Personal Experience

One of the saddest aspects of life can be the feeling of being alone in the world and no more so than for someone with ASD.

It's important to note that loneliness, although often amplified for people with ASD, especially HFA, can affect all types of people. Loneliness can also be combated and resolved with determination and effort. I want to tell you a little about my experience and battle with being lonely.

I have always been reclusive and insular. Even when I performed I would do so with an explosion of energy and interact with the audience but off the stage I was a different matter. I always described myself as a "Jack in the box". I am sure that some people would see me as outgoing, however, that is just the surface. My job over the years, through my own lack of action and resolution, has actually reinforced the feeling of being alone.

I would perform in front of and teach many people. It is a two-way impersonal transaction. I have performed in front of 20,000 people who were going wild and then a few moments later had nobody to talk to at all and felt lonely. It's the same with dance sessions. I am the boss and the teacher and I am very professional. I teach and then I leave. They don't talk to me on a personal level. On the other hand, I must take responsibility for the same thing. It takes two to tango.

Christmas's and birthday celebrations

I would often find myself on my own for birthdays, Christmases and New Year celebrations. I think there was a decade growing up when I spent ten Christmases in a row on my own. Part of me felt relief at this but I have cried many times out of isolation and loneliness, wishing that I had somebody to share those times with.

Unfortunately, it wasn't to be. Fortunately you can work on it.

It takes time but you can change your environment. The first half of my life's celebrations were quite sporadic, often at different foster homes, or special centres for children or in a step family. After I ran away, I didn't actually have anybody to spend the time with, so it was just a default to be alone and be upset. After about ten years, friends started to invite me over to their homes but I often felt uncomfortable with that, like I was a burden. The public transport didn't run on Christmas day, so they would have to go out of their way to pick me up and I didn't like the idea of that, especially when they had their own families and special day to worry about. In addition to that, I remember when I was young being around strangers at Christmas and I didn't want to be that person disrupting someone else's special day. Later on I changed my attitude slightly and did visit friends at Christmas. I really appreciated their hospitality. However, it didn't quite feel right. I felt like an alien or an intruder. It was only a few years ago that I learned to accept and be grateful, even if I was alone.

Walking around on my own

When I look at my life, one of the things I remember most is walking around constantly with my Walkman.

I would walk twenty miles, no problem around the whole of London. I would discover "secret" parts of London! One time, I remember walking around really early in the morning – I think it was Christmas day 2004, I walked for hours and I did not see a single person. It was like a ghost town. It was very strange and eerie. However, walking was also one of the joys of my life and still is. The challenge is that it doesn't solve the feeling of being alone – you still feel very detached from society, like an observer.

Living inside your head

There was a period of many years in which I very rarely socialised and partied. I would walk around and liked going to museums alone, then I'd sleep. I would often describe myself as a person who "lives inside my head". This is a phrase that I have used for years. I live inside my head, I even choreograph dance in my head. I live a lot of my life in my head rather than in "reality", however this has changed now but I had to pro-actively work at it and change my circumstances and my preferences.

Music, books and movies

Something which I am grateful for, because it has educated and informed me so much about the arts, is my experience of music, movies and certain books. For many years I lived my life vicariously through the art. It was a completely safe space. I would read Alexander Dumas's, *The Count of Monte Cristo* on repeat. I read it repeatedly. I would write notes and highlight passages; I still have that original version too. I remember purchasing a new copy and reading the first page and instantly recognising that this was a different edit and edition. I was so used to the book that I recognised different edits and flow. This book was my education in a way. The music and the art was my education. I experienced the emotion through them. The same thing with the movies, I could escape reality and go off to another place. Music was probably the ultimate artistic experience for me though. Music, out of all artistic expression, touches me deeply and I would immerse myself in it. In a strange way the musical pieces would become my friends. Even now, when I listen to classical pieces, I feel like they are old friends. I can tell instantly what version or orchestra and how they differ to the versions I previously listened to, like children growing up. I have gotten, and still do, a lot of joy out of the arts. When you engage and interact with art it is a really good leveller. You do it solo. You don't need to be anything or know anything or understand any social rules – you can just experience and you can immerse yourself in that experience – escapism, I guess, is one way to look at it. Inhabiting a "safe space", might be another.

Social interaction

My natural default life position is to refuse most kind of socialising or social interaction. This is the automatic natural response. I see that many people, after they finish work, go for drinks in the pub and the question probably goes "Do you want to go for a drink after work?" or, "Me and the boys are going for a drink after work, do you want to join us?". My answer, compulsively, would be a definite "no". This is before I even consciously analyse the potential scenario and ask myself if I actually want to go and socialise.

Wanting to actually go and socialise, to me is irrelevant. That has never been a consideration. I probably wanted to go, I just didn't want to go through the process of socialising. It probably makes me slightly uneasy and uncomfortable too. The procedure of pretending to enjoy small talk with somebody I'm not interested in or don't care about is too tiresome. It is not appealing. If I look back, I also notice the slight feeling of fear too – that's more unconscious though. I am fully aware that I am capable of any kind of social interaction – however, having the desire to go through with it, is a totally different matter. But I am also aware that there are wonderful, amazing, interesting people that are kind and stimulating so I have changed over the years. And so can you.

Cinema

One thing that I noticed recently was that for most of my life I went to the cinema on my own… and I loved it! In fact, I remember the films I have seen in the cinema and am aware that when I'm alone I become completely immersed in the production and taken away on an imaginative journey. If I compare those experiences of going to the cinema on my own and to the times when I have gone with friends or with partners or a date, I am acutely aware that I can't recollect the film as much. I'd rather watch the film on my own and then afterwards I can give my date or friend 100% attention!

I do feel that when alone I absorb my surroundings better. I have worked hard at moving away from this dualistic way of thinking and taking it all as life's experiences, however, sensory overload and limitations are a factor and at the very least I find it prudent to plan and to almost "psyche" myself and prepare myself for certain outings and adventures.

Planning

If I don't know the person extremely well I do not like to go on spontaneous adventures. If I trust and know the person, I love it! It's like this; if I know I will be accepted and won't have to "act" and say certain words and the social nonsense, then I can enjoy it! However, if I have to do the song and dance and the social stuff with all those words and all that acting, I need time to prepare and be ready for it. This way, I can do the act, be social and look the part, even if I want to run away inside. I need to prepare for this though. The good thing is that over time, I have worked this out. Planning is key. If I'm with my trusted lieutenants though – if we pass a mountain, I'm very happy to climb it there and then! Indeed I have undertaken some amazing spontaneous trips with close friends!

Safe zones

Museums and the galleries are my safe zones. I have never spoken to anybody other than staff members in a museum or a gallery. In fact, that counts as a social experience for me. Just like the bank, the post office and the shop. They aren't just invisible events – they are social interactions for me. They take energy and still count. Maybe I should call them "micro interactions". They take up a different level of energy and effort.

Exhaustion and recovery

There is always a price to pay. Everything in life is like that and one of the prices for socialising is tiredness; for me often physical exhaustion. It doesn't matter if I wanted to spend time with the person or not, there is often a period of recovery I need to recuperate. I once went on a date with a model called Jess. I have to say that Jess was one of the most stunningly beautiful girls I'd ever seen and I couldn't even believe she wanted to go on a date with me! But sadly I messed it up. When I got home after our date I fell on the bed exhausted. I slept for hours.

After I perform a show, I sometimes escape for a few days and go for long walks alone. I need that time to recuperate. There is also a limit to my social interactions – like a capacity. There is no way I could socialise for more than three days in a row. I just need to have a couple of days to myself. Usually one day is not enough, I need a couple of consecutive days to get myself back to full strength (in a social sense) and ready to face "people" again. I don't talk on a professional level – only on a social personal level. The irony of life is that you actually do want to interact with human beings and not feel lonely, however the process, being so painful often is too costly. It's a cycle that needs to be gently broken and changed.

Insular people?

Many people on the spectrum are known as reclusive and insular. They are often considered odd, loners or eccentric. This preoccupation with their own agenda and pursuit of what gives them comfort and relief is often a solo journey or one which another might not be interested in, or understand. Consequently, some on the spectrum will have a strong need to withdraw from certain aspects of society for some peace and solitude.

Although often inclined to be alone and isolated, this does not mean that one on the spectrum is not aware of others and their lives and interests. In fact, they often crave association and social warmth and interaction but this doesn't seem possible due to the barriers, real, physical or psychological in the way due to ASD. The psychological trauma involved is often underestimated because somebody might build up the courage to finally approach and interact with another, and that in itself might be a massive victory and progression, then to find rejection or ridicule possibly because of an inability to communicate in the "usual" way or in a perceived peculiar way. They might often engage in "boring" one sided and "long" monologues about specialised subjects that others might not be interested in too which might lead to confusion when not reciprocated or appreciated. Along with all of this comes stress, pressure and confusion which is why many on the spectrum choose to be "loners", even though they wish deep in their hearts for an alternative better solution. They often want to have friends! They want to be social! They want to be loved! They want to meet people! They want to play a part in the lives of others! They want to be accepted for who they are!

We are not stupid. We know that awkwardness, insensitivity or indifference to others, "strange" or unexpected facial reactions or body language won't make it easy for us. We know that it will cause problems and we'll probably not be understood or be misinterpreted. This leads ultimately to saying "What's the point?" or "It's not worth the pain, I'll just sit on my own". What tragedy. It's a trap. Fortunately, there are techniques and things that we can do to help, which we will look at later in this book – so keep hope alive! It's sometimes hard to have faith when confronted with daily rejection and confusing mixed signals and this leads to many on the spectrum to *chronic frustration*.

Chronic frustration leads to spiralling considerations often leading to depression and mental illness. It's important to understand that people on the spectrum, like everyone else in society, want to be included. It's just that they don't know how to go about it, which leads to trouble and anxiety and often an attitude of surrender, resigned to the "fact" that they were born a "misfit" and "different".

There is a big difference between ASD and lack of social understanding and abilities as compared to somebody being "shy". An autistic person's brain will process social information differently and often misinterpret social cues and meaning that others may naturally be able to decode intuitively. This by itself is tiring and challenging. On the other hand, a shy person processes the situation in a normal fashion but due to other psychological factors, like low self-esteem may experience anxiety. People on the spectrum may also be shy, but aren't necessarily. On the other hand many autistic people are very outgoing and other somewhere in between.

- Advice and Tips

1) Face your fears head on

This will take effort and energy. You need to make a conscious choice, accept in advance, that this will be a challenge and embrace it. Educate yourself in social ways! Read personal development books and self-help books. Read every positive thinking book you can and condition yourself to be positive – what have you got to lose? What you think at this moment is not all that exists and things can and will change. Take baby steps and build a social experience filled with positive interaction. Give it time but make small progressions and move in the right direction. Don't be harsh on yourself and remember that people on the spectrum do sometimes have serious challenges in this department but that you are not alone because MANY people have this challenge. We all interact with the world and although you may feel like an alien at times, even you, still interact with the world. It's about choice. Let's choose action!

2) Friends, family and acquaintances are key

You must force yourself, if it is hard, to interact with your friends, family and acquaintances socially. This means that you need to be open to things that you don't naturally like or want to do. You might not like going out with friends but you have a goal to achieve and you are training yourself every time you go out and interact with them. Explain to your friends that you need their help and encouragement. Bring them in on the plan. In fact ask a friend to become an almost "mentor" that will encourage you.

3) Be honest with people whilst "practising and rehearsing"

If you go out with your friends see it as practice and a rehearsal. This technique might help and you might even enjoy yourself if you detach yourself slightly in this way! Ask your friends to speak with people and to guide you. In fact if you talk with somebody with a friend and it does not go the way you intended or you make a mistake or say something wrong, then your friend can help, along with yourself and explain to the person that you have ASD and that you are trying to expand developmentally and practise your social skills by talking to people. Most people (not all), but most, will be kind and understanding and even very willing to help. No matter what response you get, it is valuable practice in interacting with people – this is a good thing. Remember that this is a long-term development, it won't happen straight away. You will see that, over time, you will gain confidence and get better socially and then, as if almost miraculously, you'll be more likely to start enjoying yourself!

Just remember one thing – be kind and be authentic. Even if you say to someone, "I feel really scared right now because I'm not used to speaking with people", I promise you, you will be shocked at the reply – people are kinder than you think when you are honest with them.

4) Hang out with people with similar interests

You might feel slightly more comfortable around people who like the same things as you. You, at the very least, have that common bond which can be a catalyst for further communication and interaction.

5) Strict rule – move outside your comfort zone regularly!

You have to push boundaries. Do so in a controlled way. Say, once a week – go to a bar with a friend. Yes, you might hate it or feel uncomfortable… at first… but you need to get out and this type of activity will help. Do something you don't want to do socially – just do it! You will survive, so you can afford to push and expand your horizons. Completely disregard how you feel. Let's say you go out (reluctantly) once a week. That's fifty-two occasions. You're guaranteed to have fun and meet people on at least ONE of those fifty-two occasions!

6) Strict rule – go outside once a day

You MUST leave the house, even for fifteen minutes – once a day. You must try and interact with the world. You can walk around the park and don't have to speak with anyone. Just absorb the environment, breath the air. Touch the grass or a tree – just connect with the environment outside your own house. This is very important and will protect you mentally as well as build up a kind of resistance and strength.

7) Methods of communication

Utilise all methods of communication, including letters, email, phone – any way to connect. Remember that often the key is the intention and meaning behind the interaction. If you have social issues, you can use these methods to connect and build trust before you talk in the flesh and interact physically. Communication, especially daily, means that you are expanding and growing.

8) Listen to others

As I said before: learn to listen. If you listen to people's problems with real care they will want to interact with you more. If you're quiet and ask them questions about themselves and listen, you will learn so much about them and they will be attracted to you.

9) Social media holidays

Take a day or two a week off from social media. Social media is not reality and often not healthy for our self-esteem. People are faking it and projecting a false impression of themselves often and if you are on the spectrum you might fall into the trap of comparison and believing their nonsense. Believe me, it's nonsense most of the time and they are just as unhappy and insecure as you. Disengage and unplug for a couple of days a week. It will do wonders for you. Replace it with a positive book or even meeting up with a real life friend.

Chapter 13

Living with Asperger's

Words, Communication and Interpretation

- Personal Experience

Over the years my communication skills have evolved drastically. I'm especially talking about my interpersonal skills. I have improved my understanding and grasp of the meaning behind words. I have also noticed that when I am in an emotional state, tired or interacting with somebody who is illogical or unreasonable then my grasp of what is going on and the undertone has often suffered. Even to this day, I realise that it takes me slightly more effort and energy when interpreting things when I am in an extreme emotional state – even if I would usually have no problem at all. On the other hand, my use of vocabulary and grasp of the English language is perceived, by my friends, as impeccable. They often ask me to explain things and the meaning of words.

I have, by myself it seems, identified perceived problems

and formulated ways to improve. I had the ability to notice when something was wrong and resolve it. I don't like unresolved issues once a problem has been identified. I spoke about my past challenges with certain types of communication with the expert and this is what he noted:

"He tends to interpret comments people make in quite a literal sense and finds pleasantries and social skills do not come naturally to him. One of the best descriptions of his style is he has a tendency towards "concrete thinking", in other words taking the literal meaning rather than the social nuances."

Ironically, people in my close circle think that I have great communication skills. I have just trained myself over time to understand. It has been a challenge but I feel that I have consciously learned what others seem to know intuitively, to such a fast degree, that on the surface my reaction times are so quick that it seems that I am pretty "normal". However, when emotional situations occur I can get overloaded. Understanding subtext can be hard in those situations – sarcasm and insinuations especially.

Other Frustrations:

How are you today?

This is a question, which until very recently confused me greatly. I didn't understand the question. I didn't understand why people wanted to know about my internal situation. I didn't know why they asked and I didn't know why they asked when I could see that they never listened to the answer!

Good morning!

This is another one which kind of frustrated me. Why are they saying "good morning" all the time? They look miserable, so obviously it isn't a "good morning" at all.

Enjoy your meal!

Maybe I don't want to enjoy my meal! Why do you even care if I enjoy my meal! You don't. So why say it? Tell me you hate your job. I will then sincerely enjoy my meal and appreciate your honesty. However, whether I enjoy my meal or not is nobody's concern but mine and I don't like being told to do things. Don't presume anything. Let me eat in peace.

Have a nice day!

Don't even get me started with this one…

What are you doing here?

I would often come into the dance studio to go to my locker or meet with somebody and a member of staff behind the desk would look at the schedule and say, "Oh! What are you doing here?" ... every single time. My internal reaction, internally, is "I've been here for fifteen years which is fourteen years more than you, so maybe I should be asking you, what are you doing here?" But I'd smile and say, "Just passing by and using the bathroom." Their confused face would then be satisfied and I could then proceed once this false interaction has taken place, until the next time, when we do the song and dance again. Such pointless false interactions are tedious but seemingly required for many people, for some unknown reason.

Hope you're doing better!

Hope you're doing better! What does that even mean? I have never understood the point in insincere pleasantries.

Sorry. No! You mean "Excuse me"!

Standing next to somebody and saying "sorry" is pointless and foolish. What have you done to apologise for? "Sorry" is not excuse me and never has been and never will.

Take a breath!

Wow, I need to take a breath recounting the things that used to affect me.

If you have ASD I wonder if you can relate to any of the above? Upsetting and confusing aren't they! A "normal" person must think we're nuts!

Realisation

It was my friends, Thalea and Nigel, who taught me something that I'd never realised before. These things are not to be taken LITERALLY! "How are you?" most of the time, if not an ACTUAL question, it's just a GREETING, a pleasantry! It's totally fine to talk nonsense as long as you are aware that it's just nonsense. I now KNOW they don't actually care about how I'm doing and I KNOW they don't actually want an answer. I didn't even know this for most of my life.

Every time someone says these things to me, it's a reminder of my life developmental progress and I'm so grateful for that!

Best friend telling jokes

Simon, when telling a joke, about one or two seconds later will look at me and say, "I'm joking, Anthony." I will then laugh at the joke. This is not because I'm faking it and think that I should laugh but I need those seconds to calculate the words I've heard and like a computer, establish the intent and nuance and realise that they go into the humour department. Over time, I get better with these things though and I feel totally fine.

Communication that is efficient

I really like communication which is quick, efficient and pointed. For example, during any kind of conflict resolution, I like productive conversation rather than negative backwards talk. If somebody wants to vent frustrations, then that is fine because that is a means to an end and part of the process but it needs to be with an eye on the solution, otherwise, what's the point? I also find myself being direct and truthful, even when it is detrimental to my own interests. I'm known for this and respected for it. So, I'd never "cheat" on my partner. I always feel that you don't cheat them – you cheat yourself.

Repeating myself

Jacqui would tell me that I would often repeat myself. It's definitely true. Part of me thinks that because she never really listened to what I said but I am aware that I do repeat myself in other areas of my life too. She really forced out a lot of issues in me which we will take a look out.

- Tips and Advice

1) Read, read and read even more!

Educate yourself on all potential problems you might have, with regards to interaction and interpretation and meaning, so that you are aware of the challenge.

2) Inform yourself

Don't be afraid to use Google and decode words, phrases and double meaning! Increase your vocabulary – don't let any phrase go! If you FEEL any kind emotion and confusion when you have heard a phrase or are unsure, then THAT is an indicator to CONFIRM or learn a new phrase or meaning. Use your emotion as an indicator to expand as a person. Purchase books and ask people to explain, if you don't know what "raining cats and dogs" means. It's alright not to know first time, however, second time make sure you've thought about it and found out, if possible! If you read about many of the most famous phrases in advance it will help you in understanding.

3) Practise practise practise!

Constantly practise your methods of communication and ask questions! Rehearse with friends and family – especially with people with no emotional attachment. (Make sure this is done safely or with a friend.) Let me give you an example. You have an emotional connection to your boss at work, so you might not want to practise on them. However, if you're walking down the street and a charity worker approaches you, than instead of ignoring them you can use this as an opportunity to expand your skills and learn about what they have to say. You can speak with them and they are paid to listen and interact and you have nothing to lose! It's purely an exercise, so you can ask them how their day was etc. Afterwards, you can tell them that you have

ASD and that you wanted to talk with them to practise and can they give you any feedback and advice. ANY feedback will be good feedback. Then incorporate that, speaking with trusted friends and family, adjust and continue. Practice makes perfect!

4) Listen

In fear of repeating myself: this will change your life. Many you of you will relate to this: often we speak and then instead of listening, we are just waiting to speak again. This is detrimental to our own mental wellbeing and relationships and interactions. I learned this and actively monitored myself and was shocked. I now focus on listening as a goal in itself! Conversation needs to be authentic and two-way. Monitor yourself and try to make adjustments. Out of everything, this has the potential to change your relationships and also cut down your stress levels. People on the spectrum often have challenges knowing when to speak and reply or when to interject. Listening increases the chances of accuracy!

5) If in doubt about anything ASK!

Nothing more to add to this!

6) If in doubt, see a doctor!

Sarcasm – it's a common thought that people on the spectrum don't understand sarcasm. I find that I understand it most of the time and will often make a quick determination as to whether it was used. If you find that your life quality is being inhibited by any kind of communication challenge then you should go and see your doctor or an expert. However, I'd suggest that many people that use excessive sarcasm might also want to see a doctor too!

7) Say what you mean and mean what you say

I naturally choose my words with accuracy so that I am understood. I mean what I say and I say what I mean. This is often a trait of those on the spectrum and it's a wonderful human quality. Embrace you directness and honesty. This is a good thing. The world would be a better place if everybody could say what they meant.

8) Be kind and keep it to yourself sometimes!

When somebody asks a question, I will give an honest answer. Sometimes this honest answer might not be appropriate. Remember what I said above, people often say what they don't mean. On the other hand I have a suggestion for you that I have implemented into my life big time and that is to sometimes keep an answer to yourself. It's better sometimes to internalise it and then to say something which might come across as less offensive. This way you can have the satisfaction of internal honesty but also be kind. Let kindness and honesty lead you.

Chapter 14

Living with Asperger's

Eccentricity and Idiosyncrasies

- **Personal Experience**

A chapter about my personal eccentricities and idiosyncrasies could easily run to a length of a book of several volumes. But you will already be able to see that many of the things already covered so I will just make you aware that these are commonplace with ASD sufferers. But maybe not just those with ASD.

Every person on this earth has their own unique quirks and personality traits. What I do find interesting is that people on the spectrum certainly have commonalities between them with regard to their behaviour

I've always had an ability to self-reflect and solve problems. At the very least, I've got a very good ability to identify problems. I guess this is something to with having fend for myself from a very young age. Adversity in an odd way trains you for life and grounds you. So, when I look at myself and think about my own oddities I have absolutely no problem listing them and analysing them. They are just part of who I am. But what's amazing is we can change them! Some things will take longer than others. Many eccentricities and idiosyncrasies of somebody with ASD are obvious, but many are not. I've mentioned many in this book. Here are a few other ones!

OCD

Over the years I've had many traits of OCD. I identified many of them and worked on resolving them. Many people with ASD also have traits of OCD. I have far fewer now.

Obsession

I certainly have an obsessive element to my personality. If I'm reading about a subject, I tend to read everything that exists about it. If I listen to an Erik Satie piece of music and love it, I will acquire every version that exists and his full works and read books about him. Same with Beethoven, Mozart and of course Michael Jackson. Same when I wanted to learn painting. When I read *The Count of Monte Cristo*, I decided that I wanted every version of the movie from the French language TV series version to the 1964 version, to the cartoon version to the movies – every single one that exists.

Driving a car

I don't know how to drive and I have never learned and have no desire to learn. Is this odd? Has this got anything to do with ASD? I'm unsure …

Pattern recognition

I have a tendency to notice things. I will notice when you've changed your make-up, your perfume, plucked your eyebrows, cut your hair. I can see when the media are hyping something up for a particular reason (like beating the war drum). I notice the small things like shoes, socks or your watch. When I look back, I sometimes forget a face but I will never forget the socks. I'm also good at understanding body language, especially when I am not emotionally attached to the situation.

Memory for strange things

I tend to remember very distinct details about certain things such as obscure things from childhood and later.

For example, I remember when a social worker saved me the aeroplane walker toy when I was six years old. He knew that I liked it and put it aside so that when I was dropped off, I could play with it. I am still grateful for this.

- **Official Perspective**

Many people living with ASD are perceived as being different, odd or eccentric. Traits can include repetitive behaviour and obsessions. Often those of us on the spectrum have a particular topic which we are interested in and often an expert in as we have a curiosity and need to learn everything about certain subjects and topics we are attracted to. Sometimes people on the spectrum talk about their chosen topic of interest and only talk about that.

All of the peculiarities in language and speech, repetitious rituals or routines coupled with often socially or emotionally inappropriate behaviours and bad communication skills, inhibiting "normal" levels of successful interaction can be perceived as odd and eccentric by some people. One of the diagnostic criteria for Asperger's is, "encompassing preoccupation with one or more stereotyped and restricted patterns of interest that is abnormal either in intensity or focus." When I think of this in regard to myself, I think immediately of my ability to listen to almost any Michael Jackson concert and name the country it was performed in. I don't even need to hear the music, just the crowd. Who the hell needs to know this in any normal worldly situation? However, it works well for me because it reinforces the work that I do, so ultimately it makes sense and I can use it to my advantage as an expert in this field of dance, music and performance. However this attention to detail can be challenging because some on the spectrum can find it hard to accept change or have flexibility in routine or schedule. People might not understand that the routines are needed. Also something, which I don't personally have an issue with, is certain mannerisms or body movements that might be perceived as strange. One thing which I used to do a lot was click my fingers when dancing. I clicked them so much that I would cut my finger. For many years I had an open wound on my finger due to the contact clicking. I have toned it down but the skin is still slightly thicker on that particular finger. I can get away with this more readily because it works in the context of my work, however, others might not be so lucky i.e. if somebody wants to click and they are in an office, it might not be interpreted in the same way!

People with autism have many different obsessions but

some of the more common ones include computer games, trains, historical dates or sports events, science, or TV programmes. Sometimes people on the spectrum develop obsessions with things like car registration numbers, train timetables, bridges, traffic lights, numbers and shapes etc.

People with autism may also become attached to actual objects such as toys or models or unusual objects like stones, stickers, marbles or shoes. An interest in collecting is also quite common: it might be certain books or comics, brochures, insects, leaves or an unlimited number of "weird" things!

- **Tips and Advice**

Eccentrics: *A Study of Sanity and Strangeness* is a book written by Dr David Weeks. He claims that his study "was the first and, to this day, the only scientific investigation of eccentricity". He came to some really cool conclusions for people like us, including; that "eccentrics" are physically healthier and significantly happier than "normal" people. That's pretty cool, don't you think?

Top Tips:

1. Embrace your eccentricity

Embrace the positives about yourself, including your interests, eccentricities and idiosyncrasies. Be proud that you are not a conformist and just another clone!

2. Work to remove unnecessary ones or damaging ones

If you feel that something about you may be really odd or "weird", self-reflect and ask yourself, "Is this behaviour damaging me in anyway?" If so, alter or refrain from that activity. Communicate with trusted friends and ask them to warn you if they are concerned about anything and to look out for you. Have at least one trusted friend who you confide in and tell your secrets.

3. Analyse yourself

It's really important to self-analyse and understand yourself to grow and develop as a person. It will take effort and hard work but nothing in your life will be more rewarding in the end.

4. Family and Friends – Communication is key

Communicate with your family and friends if your innocent non-harming behaviour is an issue. Your family, through understanding of ASD and Asperger's education will eventually understand and come to accept you for who you are.

5. Don't be afraid to consult experts

If you are curious and want to investigate any oddities in your behaviour then do not be afraid to consult a psychotherapist or a similar expert – some are absolutely amazing!

Chapter 15

Living with Asperger's

Talent

- Personal Experience

Life is challenging with or without having ASD, but there are positives! One of them is often perceived as "Talent". I have a slightly different opinion: I believe that hyper focus, excellent absorption and obsession equal what is often perceived as talent. I take this to anything I apply my mind to. Not just dance and artistic endeavours.

Website in a night

I was working on an artistic project and we had employed a web designer. He was slow and becoming, very quickly, a waste of time. I was so annoyed that, with no HTML experience or training, I learned and designed a website in HTML overnight. I put that one out and told the team later, after I'd been awake all night, that I had decided to do the job myself. I just did the research, absorbed it and completed it. This is something that I know I can do well. Training and education really is overrated on occasion. When we get a website created now, we will still use an expert, however they know and I know that if needs be I can step in and address most issues – and this means they can't mess around as much.

Authors note: As an advocate of child protection who is strongly against child abuse and inappropriate behaviour towards children, I decided to stop all association with Michael Jackson when certain allegations became known. I have kept the following paragraphs to demonstrate a particular point only and disavow my previous associations with Michael Jackson.

Practice or natural talent?

I've taught professionally for the last thirteen years. In fact I've been performing and teaching professionally on the stage since I was about thirteen. In 2004 Michael Jackson kindly recommended my classes on his website. I remember when I did a project for Sony PlayStation, Michael Jackson's famous choreographer emailed me and said how amazing what I was doing was – I was so shocked and happy! I've taught so many celebrities and featured so much in the media over the years. I co-choreographed a west end show about Michael Jackson and my backslide lessons has over 36 million views on YouTube. I created DVDs and wrote a book on dance … you'd think that I was born with this talent, right? Wrong!

Michael Jackson dance contest

As somebody who has created a niche as being the number 1 Michael Jackson dance expert in the world, this is going to sound very ironic and funny.

I was in North Wales in a place called Rhyl. There was a "Michael Jackson Dance Contest" and they were playing 'Bad'. They invited ten children onto the stage to dance, one at a time. I was called up and I danced. What place out of the ten do you think I came? Number 1 right? Wrong! I came tenth. I didn't know what I was doing and I got booed off the stage. I didn't particularly know anything about Michael Jackson or dance. That was to change in the next couple of years! So, the lesson is this: I wasn't born with it. I learned it. I absorbed it.

Television

I've always had the ability to talk very confidently on television. I guess this is because I was adopted off a television show! Fast forward twenty years and whenever *Sky News* had a Michael Jackson story they would often call me as their on screen "expert". I appeared so often and there were times when I was abroad when I could appear and other times when I was in Scotland, for example, that they sent a live satellite truck to meet me so I could be interviewed live. They knew they could trust me. I knew exactly what to say. It was hot wired into me. They could ask me any question about Michael's performance and I would know the answer. I would do it confidently and speak with authority. This is why they always called me back. This in itself is a learned talent.

- Official Perspective

According to *The Economist* magazine in the UK, "There is strong evidence for a link between genius and autism" and others have discovered strong links between savant syndrome and autism. Films have been made about it, like *Rain Man* and numerous documentaries. A study by a doctor from Kings College London has even suggested in a study that up to 30% of people on the spectrum have a "sort of savant-like capability in areas such as calculation or music". It's important to note that not all children or people on the spectrum will be a savant or a genius.

So many creative artistic types over the years have displayed symptoms associated with ASD from obsessive qualities to being a recluse to "eccentric" behaviour. I think that the key thing a person with ASD does, is focus on details and have an obsession with absorbing and learning "everything about a subject" and thus becoming an expert in it.

Laurent Mottron, a professor in the Department of Psychiatry at the University of Montreal found that, "people with autism who have average IQ scores are nonetheless up to 40% faster than their peers without autism at solving complex logical problems" and that "people with autism possess enhanced perceptual abilities: they excel at discerning patterns against the backdrop of complex environments, spotting embedded details that others miss, and often have exceptional ability in mentally manipulating 3D shapes" and "enhanced activity in people with autism in brain regions associated with visual processing, object recognition, visual imagery and visual expertise, the ability to differentiate between similar objects — for example, different types of birds".

It's generally understood that many of the most talented and famous people from history might have very well been on the spectrum. These people include scientists, artists, politicians and geniuses from all walks of life. Including; Albert Einstein, Amadeus Mozart, Sir Isaac Newton, Charles Darwin, Michelangelo, Hans Christian Andersen, Andy Warhol and in my opinion the most obvious of them all but not publicly acknowledged yet, French composer, Erik Satie.

- **Advice and Tips**

1) Look to those you admire already

Try this trick! Think of the people you are a big fan of and admire. Maybe they are an artist, a musician, an actor, a scientist or a politician and find out what THEIR interests were. They probably have/had a variety of interests and talents that aren't publicised.

2) Force yourself to try something new

Make a list of your possible untapped talents and skills. You will be shocked because you probably, no.... you *definitely* have talents in areas you haven't discovered yet!

3) Push yourself – don't let talent go to waste!

Embrace your "weird" interests and make sure you don't fight against them! They are probably one of the biggest blessings of your life!

5) Express yourself in all the ways you can

Make sure that you express yourself in all the ways you wish and want to before you die. Most people don't and leave it until it's too late. Don't make that mistake – express yourself and your talents while you have the chance and make sure you enjoy the experience too. If you need help and assistance, ask a friend for advice and support. You can even say to a friend, "I need some encouragement with regards to this." Believe in yourself and others will believe in you. If they don't believe in you (or they do), it's not even relevant. They will believe after you have proven them wrong and respect you and admire you!

Chapter 16

Living With Asperger's

Staying Well

I told you at the beginning of the book that I was going to speak from personal experience. The next few paragraphs have the potential to transform your life and potentially to make living with ASD significantly easier. These things worked for me and they may work for you.

Fitness

Fitness and exercise affect my feeling of wellbeing and ability to interact with the world. My usual exercise is running. I don't count my dancing as exercise because that's also a mental activity; I am usually teaching as well as moving. With running, I can just run. I used to run up to ten miles per day but I found, after a time, that this took too much out of me. So now I can run an hour pretty easily and still feel fresh and strong throughout the day. Exercise produces endorphins which lift our mood. I also see running as a social activity, even though I don't speak with anybody. I see people, I interact with them and this is a good thing because it reminds me that I am part of a wider society.

I have no experience with this but I also understand that some of us diagnosed can experience coordination and balance challenges and I suspect that regular activity can probably help improve this.

It goes without saying that any regular fitness activity will improve your self-confidence. If you incorporate a fitness routine, which you are comfortable with and enjoy, you will receive significant benefits to your outlook, mood, health and general wellbeing.

Sleep

When we're tired it doesn't help us interact with the world in a happy way. So it's important that you get enough sleep. How much sleep is a personal thing based upon your own body and your own activity. You want to sleep until you feel rested and then wake up. It's probably not a good thing to sleep for less than nine hours regularly but you should experiment and see what amount of rest helps you to feel best. For me, as you know, the way I am awoken is extremely important.

I have read that many children with Asperger's sleep walk and I find this interesting because I regularly did this when I was younger. I sometimes still do. Get into a relaxed state prior to sleep – this might include not having a television or other screens on in the bedroom.

Food

We are what we eat and I have experimented for weeks with different diets and different foods and this is what I can report:

- Sugar

Cutting sugar out will change your life. When I cut sugar out, I felt like a different person. My mood changed, as much as I became more patient and more tolerant. When people around me made noise, I didn't react as quickly as when I consumed sugar. I also felt more energetic and more stable.

- **Processed foods**

I cut out processed foods and replaced them with, as best as I could, organic healthy "real" food. People commented how bright and vibrant I looked and I just felt more peaceful and that I could handle the world better. I understand that gluten can affect people on the spectrum, and this may be so, but what I can say is that cutting all the processed stuff out completely transformed the way I felt for the better.

- **Milk and meat**

I found that I had to reduce my running from ten miles a day because my energy levels, without meat, were significantly lower until I replaced meat with fish. Cutting out the dairy also helped me feel better and fresher.

- **Incorporating all of the above**

When I incorporated all of the above, I often described it as "life changing" and feeling like a "new human being". I found myself feeling that the ASD was less a part of me and had less affect. I felt that I was less emotional and less reactive. Experiment with what works for you. Whatever you consume, consume it consciously and take note of how you feel that day and the next day. If you need to keep a diary.

Chapter 17

Living with Asperger's

Other Coping Strategies

We've already looked at some possible options with regards to health, nutrition and fitness. Now we're going to look briefly at some other strategies.

Meditation

I have mediated for hundreds of days consecutively. I can say with my hand on heart it has been life changing! However, before I tell you about the specific mediation I do, I would encourage you, if you wish to meditate, to find one that you are comfortable with and works for you. You can look online or in books. Another thing you can do is just sit peacefully. Turn off the electric gadgets and phones as well as the lights and just sit for a few moments and be peaceful. You will be surprised how many ways this benefits you.

Another brilliant way of relaxing the brain is to find a peaceful meditative piece of music, say, Erik Satie's relaxing 'Gymnopedies' and again, turn off all the lights and gadgets and just sit and listen. I currently mediate for around forty minutes each day, however I'm going to tell you about an easier one that I did for many days.

It's called "Isha Kriya" from an Indian Yogi called "Sadhguru". He looks the part! If you want a meditation you want one from a guy that looks like this! You can do a short thirteen minutes per day and it's in three parts. You just sit on a chair and essentially repeat (internally) to yourself, "I am not the body … I am not even the mind", then you make a certain sound, then you sit peacefully. You can find out more yourself online through the Isha Foundation or find an alternative meditation that may work for you. If you can't find one then feel free to make one up!

Control surroundings and environment (recuperate and safe spaces)

It's very important that you create a "safe space" in your life where you can recuperate and relax without being disturbed, for an amount of time which you feel recharges your batteries. I would suggest that you do whatever you need to do to make it the best it can be. Fully soundproof a space if you must, just make sure that you have a place in your life to retreat to when things get too much.

Controlling your environment is probably the best way to reduce the challenges that often come with ASD. If you can remove yourself from noise and threats then this is the best way – by creating distance. However, if this is not possible, you can often create a "barrier". This can be a physical barrier, for example to block noise, but also a psychological barrier. For example, let's say there is noise from behind a wall and you have tried your best to reduce the sound, you may want to resort to placing a large sheet or a sleeping bag (I have done this before) over the area, this is like a block. Or move if an environment really doesn't work. Don't be afraid of change as this will improve the quality of your life.

Retrospective analysis

It is of utmost importance that you look at your own behaviour and your own challenges and analyse them. Why exactly are you upset? What caused it? Was it physical pain? Was it real or in your mind? You must reflect because then you can look at why you were, say, feeling down and address any external or controllable factors for the future, thus reducing your discomfort and making your life easier.

Get up to date medical attention and any psychological help

Make sure that you see the doctor regularly and keep up to date with your check-ups and medication. Also, do not be afraid to ask for any kind of psychological help you may need..

Cultivate human real world relationships

Remember that you must try as hard as you can to put time aside to cultivate real world friendships and relationships. Don't be afraid to open up to friends and family and "vent".

Chapter 18

Frequently Asked Questions

Do people with ASD have empathy?

Of course! In fact, according to 2009 study people on the spectrum have more empathy than "normal" people!

What causes ASD and could be something from our past?

ASD is not caused by emotional trauma, neglect or upbringing. The research is clear – ASD is a "developmental disorder due to a dysfunction of specific structures and systems of the brain". In other words: it is no one's fault.

I don't fit – what should I do?

Embrace being unique; enjoy being yourself! BUT if you are bullied you must report this to the authorities, communicate with your friends and family.

How many people are affected by Asperger's?

According to the research between 0.36% and 0.71% of the world's population is affected; which is around 68 million people. So, we're certainly FACTUALLY, not alone.

I have no friends – what do I do?

Change your behaviour and do things that might be temporarily uncomfortable so that you will start to make friends. Take responsibility.

How do I deal with loneliness?

You need to get out into the world and change your environment. Do it in small steps. Small steps will make a big difference and then build from there.

Is ASD the same as autism?

Asperger's demonstrates some of the foundation traits of autism.

ASD is considered to be on the "Autism Spectrum." ASD, Asperger's and autism involve a neuro-biological difference in how information is processed and integrated. A lot of this is just words to describe the same type of condition, which is "Autism Spectrum Disorder". This sums it up nicely: "HFA is an informal term applied to individuals with autism, an IQ of 80 or above, and the ability to speak, read, and write. HFA may simply refer to autistic people who have normal overall intelligence; that is, are not cognitively challenged." (National Institute of Health News)

Will I be alone forever? What if I want a partner?

If you don't want to be alone you won't be. There are 7 billion people on this earth. Somewhere in there, is a number of people who would work well with you and a number who would LOVE to be with somebody like you.

Can ASD Be Cured?

There is currently no cure for ASD. But do you want one? I would not want to change with a "normal" person. My friends have far more issues than me.

I've read a lot of bad things about ASD online... are they true?

Disregard the lot! The people that write this nonsense are often bitter and twisted people who use ASD as a way of projecting their own inadequacies. If you want the truth, you need to get it unadulterated, unbiased and delivered in a professional way. Start with the NAS, the NHS and official sources.

Is ASD/HFA a disability?

I'll speak from a personal perspective. I do not define myself by anything which has happened to me. I don't care about my achievements, in the sense that they don't define me. The way that I can dance, doesn't define me and the fact that I am on the spectrum does not define me. My ASD has helped me– especially with regards to morality and principles. I do not feel disabled in any way.

I'll tell you a secret – I feel the MOST "abled" out of my friends and peers because I am aware of my challenges, I work on them every day and I have an inner desire to overcome. My awareness gives me the ability to transcend any challenge or "disability".

Chapter 19

Two And A Half Years Later…

The good news is you will do just fine and get through the initial period of "discombobulation" (to put it mildly) … you'll get through it and might even come through stronger on the other side, if you really apply yourself, and most probably even if you don't!

I intentionally held back this book so I could test out my personal techniques and own advice on myself and for myself. It's two and a half years since I wrote the original manuscript and the version that you are reading is only one third of the original length. I wanted to be *sure* that what ended up in this book actually worked, would actually help and was actually of use.

I am very pleased to tell you that not only have I put this book to the test, but I have conceived some new psychological devices and techniques as well as tested them and *recorded the results*.

I am also very pleased to be able to deliver the results to you. Some worked, some didn't. I disregarded the ones that didn't practically work. Some worked for a short period of time, some were too much hard work and some were not workable.

However, in the end I think I have some good news for you and some practical tested techniques and psychological devices that might really help you as they have helped me.

The results, on the one hand, are quite shocking but on the other hand are very helpful because, as the saying goes, "to be forewarned is to be forearmed".

The Boxing Match Analogy

I came to a realisation after about two years that changing your philosophy or viewpoint doesn't help much with regards to our certain challenges related to ASD. It's not a case of waking up in the morning and deciding that you are going to positively deal with your day's challenges. I came to the realisation that this is cyclic. Then as I thought more I began to see similarities between our "challenge" and a boxing match. There are twelve rounds in a boxing match and you might win some and you might lose some. This reminds me of the daily challenge of ASD. You might have a good hour and then an extremely challenging three hours. Then another good hour etc. So this is an everyday, every hour, every moment, constantly evolving challenge that needs realistic pragmatism and honesty. It may well be a constant lifelong challenge. However, we see that it's cyclic which means that it's might be useful to have a pause between "rounds" to collect oneself. This might even be giving yourself a "pep talk" or even utilising a psychological "trick" or technique to help you. Before we get to some practical techniques though ...

Deciding Whether to Disclose your ASD

There is a great nautical saying that goes like this: 'Batten down the hatches – quick, men.' (*Chambers Journal*, 1883). It means that the weather could turn and the ship needs to be prepared and the hatches (essentially "holes") battened (meaning "covered"). Another words, it means brace yourself and be prepared! This would be the time to really consider where you are in your life, consider your surroundings, your friends and your activity and focus. Focus on the job at hand, which is to grow through this experience and be stronger and healthy and live a happy life. It is very important that this is done with discipline and awareness and also not to judge the whole world from your perspective because there might well be elements with regards to disclosure which you might not be prepared for. Either way, preparation is key and I want to now reveal some data that I have collected over the last two and a half years which may or may not be of some use to you.

The Statistics and 'The 80%'

"I was recently diagnosed with something called Autism Spectrum Disorder. It's sometimes called "High functioning Asperger's". It's relatively mild compared to some and I'm very high functioning so you might not notice it at first if you don't know me well".

This was my stock line for the last couple of years. Whenever the subject came up, or I chose (or often didn't choose), this was the choice of words I personally chose to make the disclosure. I recorded **all** of the responses.

Rating the Responses

I rated the responses and attributed a number (1 – 5), as below:

Rating 1: Dehumanising and offensive

Rating 2: Dismissive and or/and passive aggressive

Rating 3: Neutral or unresponsive

Rating 4: Normal and reasonable

Rating 5: Empathetic and kind

I then divided the responses elicited and their ratings into two very simple indicators:

1) Appropriate

or

2) Inappropriate

The Results

20% responded in an APPROPRIATE way.

80% responded in an INAPPROPRIATE way.

A Breakdown of 'The 20%': APPROPRIATE RESPONSES

*Half of the 20% responded with a "Rating 4": **Normal and reasonable***

*Half of the 20% responded with a "Rating 5": **Empathetic and kind***

A Breakdown of 'The 80%': INAPPROPRIATE RESPONSES

Half of the 80% responded with a "*Rating 1*": ***Dehumanising and offensive***

Half of the 80% responded with a "*Rating 2*": ***Dismissive and or/and passive aggressive***

(Negligible: "Rating 3": Neutral or unresponsive)

Selection Bias?

According to my data, age, gender, education, culture, race demographic etc. had very little impact on the results with the exception of one indicator. It also appears that relationship to the respondent has almost no impact on the response. It makes no difference if respondent is "friend or foe", according to my data.

Example 1: The Four Doctors

I am fortunate to have four close friends who are doctors. One is a vascular surgeon, one a retired gastroenterologist, one is a general practitioner and one is a heart surgeon. In addition, all four doctors are from different cultures and parts of the world as well as ages. Two are female and two are male.

Here is how they responded:

> *Doctor 1:* responded with a *Rating 1: Dehumanising and offensive*
>
> *Doctor 2:* responded with a *Rating 2: Dismissive and or/and passive aggressive*
>
> *Doctor 3:* responded with a *Rating 4: Normal and reasonable*
>
> *Doctor 4:* responded with a *Rating 5: Empathetic and kind*

It appears that there is no pattern whatsoever with regards to the way somebody responds … with one exception, which we will take a look at shortly. I respect all of these people for their opinion and perspective and absolutely do not take any response personally, even if

I felt it was offensive or hurtful. That is their choice and nothing to do with me and most probably totally unintentional. I am totally fine with that.

Example 1: 'Penelope' from Portugal

Penelope, from Portugal (not her real name or country of origin) walked into the cafe and saw myself and a friend talking. She sat down and asked what we were talking about. My friend told her and before long I delivered the line:

"I was recently diagnosed with something called Autism Spectrum Disorder. It's sometimes called "High functioning Asperger's". It's relatively mild compared to some and I'm very high functioning so you might not notice it at first if you don't know me well".

Penelope burst out laughing and waved her hand in a dismissive gesture and said, "You don't have Asperger's". She then said, "Let me tell you about my friend who has REAL Asperger's". When she said "real", she leaned forward towards me and smiled and gestured to touch my knee. She then told the story of her "friend", and in the middle of telling it, reiterated and *emphasised* the word "real", in "real Asperger's", leaning forward for a second time and gestured to touch my knee.

I assigned this response as a "Rating 1: Dehumanising and offensive" rather than "Rating 2: Dismissive and or/and passive aggressive" reply because of her combination of her:

- *supercilious tone of voice*
- *use of dismissive hand gestures*
- *laugher*
- *condescending demeanour and physicality*
- *reaction of friend, who looked mildly uncomfortable*

Again, I absolutely do not take Penelope's response and words personally. I kind of feel compassion and a little bit of sadness for her (and them), because I honestly don't think they knew what they were saying and the hurt they could potentially cause. I also think that that is who they are and it's their perspective and that in itself is fine. I also believe that if they knew the impact or even analysed their own words for a few moments, they themselves would realise that they probably don't really know what they're talking about and would probably be mortified by themselves and their own words. In other words, sometimes people make mistakes and say silly things and we must be understanding and compassionate and not too judgemental because ultimately it is not beneficial or particularly useful.

Specific Themes and Patterns with Responses

1) A large percentage (almost half of the 80%) directly contradicted the statement presented to them with a direct confrontation, often a very direct and definitive, "you are **not** Autistic" as a first response. There was variation in the words but always a definitive statement of *contradiction*. Something what I found very peculiar was that this was *almost always* combined with a dismissive head movement, hand gesture or laugher (or a combination of all three). It was often repeated twice. I never responded to what they said, other than to smile, which seemed to encourage them to continue to contradict my first statement. They *never* asked for any details with regards to diagnosis, doctor, additional information etc. and often didn't have any substantive personal knowledge of me. It goes without saying that almost all of the respondents had zero medical knowledge or medical education.

2) Another very prominent response was "yes but, *everybody's* on the spectrum". This was delivered by just

under half of the 80% of respondents. These responses were very often combined with a certain *dismissive tone of voice and unsympathetic speed of delivery* (i.e. almost as a "blocking technique" cutting you off and interrupting). I interpreted this combination of words and behaviour as *passive aggressive.* Another indicator was to look closely at how their statement made (or makes) you feel and the timing etc. However, more on that shortly.

3) Weaponising your disclosure: I found that about 10% of the "inappropriate" would do something very peculiar which was to, as I call it, attempt to use your disclosure as a "weapon" or as I like to put it "weaponising your disclosure". This can often be delivered in very subtle form but, using the indicators that I will soon describe, you will be able to identify it in a very short amount of time, if not instantaneously. Certain individuals will deliver your information back to you at inopportune times as; "helpful" comments or unsolicited "advice". I have no idea whether this is conscious or unconscious, but as they say, "the road to hell is paved with good intentions", so we should not take it personally and disregard respondents' motivations and only focus on OUR responses. Essentially, this response involves the respondent

pointing out a symptom (highlighting) that you may have told them in a *previous* moment of vulnerability or in confidence. This is often done at an inappropriate time, which is totally out of context and is unsolicited, i.e. it will shock you. Unfortunately, this can be used as an attempted means of control or as a means to get a "reaction" and solicit attention. Either way, it is an inappropriate imposition. Pointing to symptoms and solutions which weren't asked for, to belittle, attention seek and get a 'rise' is totally unacceptable but not unusual. Certain respondents may even do this to make you feel bad and highlight your issues as not only a way to passively attack you, but to cover for something they themselves have said or done, to shift blame under the "Pointing out help" and giving "advice" card. I also noticed that it is a great means of deflection, as one individual used it when they were in the wrong about something unrelated. They pointed my ASD out at that exact moment, with no warning and began to inquire about the symptoms and the history of it, even though they had been fully briefed a year earlier, and dismissed it all entirely at that time. They thought that that moment was a good time to deflect and passive aggressively shift the blame, avoiding taking responsibility for their misdemeanour. This is particularly manipulative and I found that approximately 5% people did this or attempted to… quite a small amount. This aligns with the statistic of 1% – 5% of people that are said to be either a psychopath or a sociopath. A very good indicator is, as I say, "look at the metadata" because timing is a very important factor in determining intentions, as well as how you feel about what they are saying… we'll come to that in a moment though.

4) One of the most peculiar responses was a kind of jealousy, direct aggression or disdain but I will explain it using another unrelated example. I once noticed a lady being very aggressive to a disabled lady, whose disability was not immediately obvious. She was aggressively "explaining" that the disabled toilets were ONLY for disabled people … she had disdain and aggression in her tone, voice and demeanour. I witnessed as my friend lifted up her colostomy bag. I saw immediate, but very brief shame in the lady's face but then something very interesting happened! I watched her "double down" and almost snarl and just walk away. It was almost like she was subconsciously disgusted with herself and instead of choosing to face it, continued to act and "fight" it, which means that she could never apologise for her behaviour and had to

pretend that she was correct. Consequently, there was a continuation or inertia of "aggression" which couldn't just then be immediately paused. Now, what I noticed is that the process of being confronted with the information actually caused a kind of "flight or fight" reaction. I also noticed that in the idea that the disability was concealed, almost like the respondent felt "tricked" and so guilty about their inappropriate reaction that they chose to continue down the road of aggression because even though they have been confronted by blatant evidence they cannot quickly backtrack because it exposes their inappropriate behaviour. That disdain that they feel is then projected onto the "victim" of the said behaviour. It's very strange but I felt that the presentation of the information elicited an aggressive response within the respondent towards THEMSELVES which then manifests itself in an aggressive or inappropriate action towards YOU.

Remember ... it's not personal!

- *They are **not** responding to you or your story, personally.*

- *Their response is actually, first and foremost, an **internal reaction** to the information presented* *only and how that relates to* **them**. *(How it makes them feel, how it makes them view themselves, what it makes them think etc.)*

- *Any visual (non-verbal) or verbal communication is a response to how they have processed the information internally within a frame of reference of themselves.*

- *Your information is only a* **trigger**.

- *They will usually respond* **unconsciously** *immediately and that response might even shock them but shame and embarrassment might even prevent any reversal or an adjustment of behaviour at a later time.*

- *That initial response is very useful for* **you**. *It's a very good indicator in somebody state of mind, state of psychological being and whether you need to act to detach from said individual or take another course of action.*

Chapter 20

PRACTICAL ADVICE AND TECHNIQUES THE TRAFFIC LIGHT SYSTEM

I found myself very concerned with what I was widely reading with regards to people on the spectrum and the possibility of a potential issue with regards to discernment and naivety and the fact that this could be taken advantage of by certain types of people. I decided to take a closer look and created a technique which, in my opinion, goes a little way in circumventing possible cognitive dissonance and denial, which would obviously be a potential concern when addressing any such issue. When looking at potentially sensitive circumstances, which may result in emotional pain, shock or trauma, many people will actually often deny the problem exists, with an inability to accept reality.

Discernment challenges and potential naivety?

We want to firstly:

1) Identify the problem

2) Identify its effects

3) Deal with the problem at the root and if possible remove the cause completely

The specific issue that I wanted to deal with head on was the potential "discernment and potential naivety" issue and its effects. First things first...

I **thought** about the potential problem

This is a good start ... but a terrible finish! I learned very quickly that you must write these things down because, let's face it, if your brain alone is good enough to work out the problem, it wouldn't have helped create the problem and it certainly would have solved it already. The potential problem is concealed so we need to **convince ourselves** with clear EVIDENCE. It's crazy when you think about it. We need to be **convinced** of what **is** because our brains can play games with us and it should play games because it helped cause the mess! However, our brains are also great because the truth always resonates within us and eventually will have an effect and somehow play out … we want it to play out to our advantage and to help us grow and live a happy, fulfilled and healthy life.

Possible discernment and naivety challenges and its effects

1) I conceived a technique to write down the "problem" ("Possible discernment and naivety challenges and its effects") and a way to clearly see the issue on paper, ***physically****.*

2) I collated the data, ***physically****.*

3) I applied the conclusions from the data directly and enthusiastically.

4) I measured the results.

The system I devised to identify possible discernment and naivety challenges and its effects on people is called, "The Traffic Light System".

The Traffic Light System STEP 1:

Be in a Calm State – in a Peaceful Place

When you are in a calm state, find a peaceful quiet place to go and sit down. I suggest that you haven't eaten a large meal within two hours of doing this, and possibly even cut out the caffeine from a couple of hours before too. You want to be a relaxed as possible with a clear mind as possible. You don't to be disturbed for a couple of hours at least and you want to do this on a day when you can relax afterwards.

Get a Pen and Writing Pad

You will need a pen and paper. If you don't want to use a pen and paper then please go and get one anyway!

.... however!

If you *really* don't want to use a pen and paper, you can use a word processor or a computer program like Word or Notepad. If you choose to do this, then make sure you create a clearly marked folder "The Traffic Light System" and place that folder on your desktop in a clear corner of the screen. You want this to be treated with respect because this is important and it's YOUR life. Don't just save files and have them all over your computer. Everything neatly in one folder and respectfully positioned IF you're not going to use a classic pen and paper. I strongly urge you to do *that* first, and then later resubmit the information you are going to write down into a computer. There is benefit in the physical action of writing.

Create a List

Think about your life and the people in it. Think about those people. Your friends, your family, your colleagues, your relationships, your acquaintances … think about them. Think about their names. Think about their faces. Think about their physicality. Now write them down in a list. Literally a long list of names. Start the list with people in your immediate life right now. Somebody nearby physically. Then maybe your mother and father. Then maybe your boyfriend or girlfriend. If you haven't got a boyfriend or girlfriend, then you can write down an ex-partner. If you haven't got an ex-partner write down somebody that you really liked. Write down their name and think about that. Think about their look… you want to SEE them in your mind. Write down your best friend and then write down all of your best friends in your life. The list should be getting pretty lengthy now. However, it won't be unmanageable.

So now you have a list which will include:

Your partner and all of your ex partners
Your best friend and all of your ex best friends
Your family

Your work colleagues
Your acquaintances
Your enemies
Key people in your life
Your associates

You can add anybody else you interact with or have interacted with in any kind of meaningful way… within the last ten to twenty years. If you want to go back fifty years, do that. If you need to ask whether somebody specifically merits addition to the list, that means that they should be added to the list. If in doubt, add them. If the list is long, that's fine.

The List

You should now have a very random list of people in and from your life. It might be long, it might be short but ultimately this list is a list of your personal links, bonds and associates. In a way, it's a historical document, but it's *your* history. Did you notice that you might have felt a range of emotions when you visualised their names and physicality? Before we move onto the next step, have a look at your list and add any names that you may have forgotten. Those emotions and feelings are very important so don't worry about feeling too happy or upset or emotional about them, we'll deal with that in a moment.

The Traffic Light System STEP 2:

Put Your List Aside

If you wish, you can do this on a separate day to "step 1", however, it's up to you. You will have created a long list of people you like and people you dislike. People you love and people you hate. Put it aside now. If it's possible, put aside your feelings and emotions because we will address those shortly but for now, we have another task to do.

Get Your Pen and Paper

Get your pen and paper out and copy these questions down (make sure it's a separate sheet of paper):

Question 1: How do I feel around this person *emotionally*. Good or bad?

Question 2: Do I feel "good" about *myself* around this person?

Question 3: Do I truly *like* this person?

Question 4: Do I characterise this person as a "nice" person?

Question 5: Does this person scare me?

Question 6: Does this person make me feel uncomfortable?

Question 7: Do I feel healthy around this person?

Question 8: Do I feel healthy *after* being around this person?

Question 9: Do I have a headache when I associate with this person?

Question 10: Do I feel like I can be my "true self" around this person?

Question 11: Do I feel "good enough" around this person?

Question 12: Do I feel valued *around* this person?

Question 13: Does this person uplift me?

Question 14: Do I characterise this person as "negative" or "toxic"?

Question 15: Do I feel comfortable being vulnerable around this person?

Question 16: Is this person a criminal or involved with drugs or illegal activity?

Question 17: Is this person a good influence or a bad influence?

Question 18: Do you like being around this person?

Question 19: Does this person "uplift" you?

Question 20: Does this person "bring you down"?

Question 21: Do you feel the need to filter what you say around this person?

Question 22: Do you respect this person as a human being?

Question 22: Do you trust this person 100%?

Question 23: Do you consider this person "moral"?

Create a Folder on your Desktop Computer

You should now have a handwritten list of the above questions on a piece of paper and separate to that you should have a list of names. The next step is to create a folder on your computer (password protect this if need be) and label it "The Traffic Light System". Within that folder create four separate documents, in Notepad or Word or whatever program works for you… make sure they are four *separate* documents. The four documents should be *labelled* as follows:

1) Black
2) Red
3) Amber
4) Green

The Traffic Light System STEP 3:

You should open all four of the now titled documents on your computer and have your list on one side, in front of you and your questions on another side.

Then you should start with the **first** name on the list and ask each question of them, in your own mind. If you need to verbally speak it, DO IT!

However, specifically change the question from, say:

"Question 21: Do you feel the need to filter what you say around this person?"

To

"Question 21: Do "I" (insert *your* name) feel the need

to filter what you say around "**Mr or Mrs List**"? (insert *their* name)"

You should add the **first** member of the list that we are looking at and replace "this person" or equivalent expression, to that specific person. You can do so in your mind or verbally. It is up to you. What IS important that you actually ask the question.

What Will Start to Happen … and the Rules

You will notice something very interesting happening. You will resist! You may fight your own mind. You may not even "accept" what you think, feel or even say! This is totally fine. This is part of it! In fact these questions are based on feelings and emotions and should be answered quickly and instinctively. If you hesitate and doubt an answer that immediately pops into your mind, then that could be your mind starting to rationalise and cognitive dissonance kicking in. This is also fine, but we have a rule and procedure for this.

The Rule

If in doubt, go *negative.*

If you have to think about the answer, for more than

half a second, "Do I like this person?" then go negative. The questions are created to elicit an emotional unconscious response. We are not too interested in the "reasoning" and rationalisation behind said response. Now proceed through each question.

Physical Response and Facial Expression

You will probably have a physical response to your answers to these questions. Remember, it's irrelevant. We are just looking at some information and how that information manifests within you when triggered by a very simple mundane question.

Start With One Person Only

Make sure you start with one person only and then pause.

The Traffic Light System STEP 4:

Before we move on to the next step, let's take a look at the four folders that you have open on your desktop. Each folder has been assigned a colour and each colour has a very specific meaning. Take a look but don't worry about applying any meaning to them with regards to anyone specific just yet:

The Black Folder

- *Threat to your life*
- *Threat to your well being*
- *Threat to your mental well being*
- *Psychopathy, narcissist or Sociopath etc.*
- *A criminal perpetrator*
- *A scary person*
- *An enemy or somebody you feel that you hate*

The Red Folder

- *A negative influence*
- *A toxic person*
- *A horrible person*
- *Somebody that you actively dislike*
- *Somebody that you do not like (different from above)*
- *Somebody that you feel uncomfortable around*
- *Somebody you try to avoid and stay away from*
- *Somebody that is untrustworthy*

The Amber Folder

- *Somebody that you are slightly wary of*
- *Somebody that you like, but not all of the time*
- *Somebody that previously acted in a "red" manner but has changed drastically*

- *Somebody that you can't quite add to the "Green folder"*
- *Somebody that is usually nice but can have a horrible side when under pressure*
- *Somebody that has something "off" that you can't quite identify yet*
- *Somebody that you do not dislike and can see the good in them*
- *Somebody that you trust but not 100%*

The Green Folder

- *Somebody that you LOVE being around*
- *Somebody that you feel uplifted and energised being around*
- *Somebody that you love or really like*
- *Somebody that encourages you*
- *Somebody that you miss and wish you could spend more time with*
- *Somebody that you feel secure and safe with*
- *Somebody that you respect and are proud to know*
- *Somebody that you feel 100% safe around being 100% yourself*

Person One on Your List

At this stage, you might know what to do already. In fact, you might want to get started already. DO IT!

Person number one .... ADD THEM TO "THEIR" FOLDER! Don't be shy and don't rationalise and excuse your initial thoughts and feelings. In fact the opposite: be STRONG. Your brain will automatically counter this by excusing certain behaviour and rationalising and excusing. Remember, answer immediately and emotionally, based on your OWN understanding of the questions. There is no need to ask for clarification because this is a judgement based on your own understanding of the definition of those questions. However, be warned. It is irrelevant if you choose to cheat yourself and put somebody that you know is a "black" in the "green" folder because there will be real life consequences for that, so it's best that you do this honestly. Remember that this is 100% private and just for you, so it doesn't necessarily have to have any impact on your life or behaviour if you don't want it to. **NEVER DISCLOSE THIS INFORMATION. IT IS 100% PRIVATE AND FOR YOU.**

Start With the People Around You and Continue Through the List

It might be an idea to start with the most important people in your life, close to your orbit, so to speak, and then branch out through the list. However, it's totally up to you. Eventually, you will have four folders with a list of names in each. However, you may have no "blacks". This is great! As long as you are being honest and truthful and you are correct, then that is wonderful. You may on the other hand, have no "greens" … don't worry… we will work on that too! The point is, is that you have the people in your life characterised according to clear motivations and behaviours now. Your feelings are based on how you really think *and* feel about the people around you. However, what should we do now? I will explain the next step! But before I do… at this stage you might encounter some issues.

Potential Issues and the Ideal Pyramid

At this stage you might actually experience shock and horror at the distribution of colours. I must say that I was. In fact, you can visualise it like this:

The Ideal Pyramid

Imagine a pyramid split into four coloured sections:

1. *The Pyramidion*
2. *Upper middle section*
3. *Lower middle section*

4. *The foundation section*

If you are imagining this in two dimensions, it would actually be an equilateral triangle but imagine that the Pyramidion is obviously the smallest section and this is coloured **black**. The second smallest section, just below this, the upper middle section is **red**. The lower middle section, the third largest section is **amber**. The final section, the "foundation" and the largest is the **green** section.

The Inverted Pyramid

Now imagine, that the colours are switched. The Pyramidion is now green and the foundation is now black. The upper middle is amber and the lower middle section is now red. Now imagine that your pyramid (or equilateral triangle) is now *turned upside down*.

That is what you call shocking and it should be a scary sight.

If your distribution looks anything like the "inverted" pyramid, you need to address this immediately. In fact, you may very well notice that your distribution is closer to this than you would have initially thought! If it is then now is a good time to ask yourself why? Is this the first time you've noticed the people around you? Why is this? However, let's jump straight to remedial action. We can deal with those questions later!

Potentially Lifesaving and Life Changing Remedial Action

I strongly advise you to think about the results of your own thought experiment, the closer you look at the people you have around you in your life, and the people that you had around you in your life. It's important that there is a historical aspect to this so you can see how you evolve and if you learn lessons etc. If not, you can start learning from today and incorporate those lessons to changing certain behaviours or tendencies which may not be conjunctive to your wellbeing. I am not in a position to tell you what to do and I am a strong believer in that if you see the information in front of you, eventually it will seep into your life. You will do what you need to do. With that said. It's obvious and simple!

*Spend more time with your **GREEN** "lights" and completely eradicate the **BLACK** "lights" from your life*

A word about the black folder and other suggestions

I strongly suggest that you immediately and swiftly eradicate anybody from the "black folder" from your life. Do so swiftly, do so safely and do so with help and assistance if need be. They should be blocked out because if somebody is a threat to your life and wellbeing then that is a major problem. Seek help from a professional or law enforcement if you are scared to disconnect from anybody in your life. It goes without saying that the "greens" are where you want to be! Invest your energy, time, friendships and relationships in those. Be wary of the ambers but be open that they can change and people can change … however, they have their category for a reason, just remember that. Reds are a threat and also best out of your life. However, you might need to navigate a detachment in a more "politically expedient" way or even use your discernment with regards to work colleagues and situations which are difficult to remove yourself from. With these situations, you should consider the impact of proximity to said people and if need be, make a situational change … just do it, if you need so, in a controlled safe and reasonable way which works for your advantage.

An Example of Cognitive Dissonance

I knowingly mischaracterised one very text book example of a "red". This individual was a clear red and I knew it straight away. However, for whatever reason another part of me didn't want to assign them to the folder I *knew* that they should be in. I rationalised many reasons. However, I made an illicit deal with *myself*. I turned a "blind eye" to it, after admitting to myself exactly what I was doing. This is fine... however, there were consequences and eventually the said individual was robustly placed in the "red" folder due to certain behaviours of said individual. Eventually, people will revert to "type". The occupants of the "red" and "black" folders are THREATS. Threats need to be taken seriously and need to be seen as they are. Pretending that they are not there does not disable the threat or make it go away. I learned this lesson the hard way, but also took it very positively because it proved the point to myself practically. A red will act like a red, for example... and when they do, it's positive to know that you saw them for what they are accurately, even if you couldn't accept it, emotionally, straight away.

The Solution of Proximity

One of the best solutions for somebody with ASD for many challenges is "proximity". Creating distance between yourself and the noise, problem or individual. If you can walk away, or move or just create an actual physical or psychological distance from the problem source, this is often the best solution. Utilise "proximity" regularly.

Looking at the "Metadata"

Metadata is defined as essentially, "data about data". This is a GREAT way to look at things because it often removes the emotional element which can often confuse the situation. In a way, this is what the "Traffic Light System" is, it's an immediate look at the data, without too much emotional "thinking". However, you can take this deeper and can apply it to other areas of your life and interactions, especially if you are having problems in certain situations or with certain individuals. This is also a good technique to use in conjunction with the "Traffic Light System". I will give you an example which relates to another book series I authored on Michael Jackson. I noticed that the professional media reviews were very positive and in actual fact, 100% positive. However, I noticed that certain associates critiqued and pointed out their "negative" viewpoints. There you have a very good example of a "metadata" data point. Professional critics were positive yet "friends" and associates point to their negative opinions. I applied a judgement on all perspectives of "positive" or "negative" but also, "solicited" or "unsolicited", "valid or invalid" and then finally, "accurate or useful" (and also did I respect and implement any criticism).

I then compared and looked at the proportion in relation to each other and the "metadata" was brilliantly clear! In fact, if you remove the critique whether it be good **or** bad, then you can usually identify and predict the tone of the information without having to hear it, by looking at other factors, i.e. delivery, timing and tone etc. That is INCREDIBLE if you think about it! You can predict what somebody will say, regardless by looking at a combination of behaviours and their usual traits. An example; "Friends and associates" that raised "negative" opinions or critique did these things **without fail,** I noted:

- *They, without exception, started said conversation with the "negative" critique.*

- *They, without exception, pursued "negative" perspective exclusively with no positive feedback during said conversation as a counter balance.*
- *They, without exception, had an "uncomfortable" look on their face and displayed some degree of impoliteness.*
- *They, without exception, had not read the book they were critiquing (maximum one third of book).*
- *Were not professional critics or experts on said subject. In fact, were exclusively novices on said subject.*
- *Without exception, all feedback from these sources was adjudged objectively to be without merit and of no use.*
- *Their delivery, without exception, made me feel uncomfortable.*
- *Their "advice" and "feedback", without exception was unsolicited.*
- *The timing was inappropriate, without exception. (i.e. I was in the middle of something, working, getting ready or preparing, or literally clothing myself…)*

I realised that the **professional critics** were overwhelmingly **positive** yet associates and "friends" were overwhelmingly **negative**. Out of curiosity, I then looked at their traffic light "colour" and saw a correlation straight away.

The Reds and Blacks were the, without exceptions proponents of "negative criticism and points of view".

No "green" criticised at all!

None! Zero! Zilch!

That is a very important piece of information and something you should bear in mind yourself … always look at the **source and their motivations**.

Another part of looking at the "metadata" is looking at the **timing**. When did said individual choose to critique you, or point out something that would obviously upset you, or raise a "negative" point? Did they choose to do so at an inopportune time? I guarantee you, when you look at the "timing" you will see patterns with certain individuals.

Finally, when looking at the "metadata" the most important parameter is, "How do you feel?" Did said individual add value to your life or upset you (without any useful input) or just make you feel bad about yourself? If they are respectful, polite and offer constructive feedback and it is welcome, then that is acceptable. However, if you look at the "metadata", you will soon learn that certain people project their nonsense on to you and they do so with the same predictable patterns and *modus operandi*. These people need to be removed or at the least within a reasonable proximity (away from you!).

If you are asking questions about an individual or their motivations then that is enough to indicate a potential "red flag" about said individual. Their behaviour will not usually be a one off. It will probably be a noticeable pattern and trait in the person.

"Meta Data" in Summary

A good rule: "Did what the person say or do something which was not reasonable which upset you or make you angry or make you uncomfortable?" If it happens regularly then you should look closer at your association with this person and their metadata "patterns". The fact that you are asking the question is the red flag but combined with the "metadata" matrix of "timing", "proportion" (of conversation, i.e. was it 100% criticism?), the "source", the "value" and was it "solicited". You will start noticing the real feedback that is of value to you and consequently the **people** who are of value to you and disregarding those are not conjunctive to your wellbeing. It makes no difference whatsoever, what the subject of conversation is as the process is universal to anything which is important to you.

The Life Timeline

We've talked about looking at the metadata in others, however, that doesn't mean we ourselves can escape. This one is one which you can do once and it will help you give yourself a little bit of perspective and an insight into certain patterns or tendencies you may have, *over time.*

Things You Will Need:

1. *A pile of A3 pieces of paper*
2. *A pencil and pen*
3. *A roll of sellotape*

Step 1: *Go to your calendar and work out how old you! You are going to create a timeline where 1 year of your life is measured with "10 cm". So, for example, if you are 20 years old, that would be 20 x 10cm in a horizontal line and a total of 200cm or 2 metres.*

***Step 2:** Take your A3 paper and create a very long sheet, using the sellotape to secure the pieces together (on the back of the sheet, as you are going to write on the front).If you are 20 years old, you might want to make a sheet of 2 metres but also add another sheet so you have some space towards the left, and right, of the timeline.*

***Step 3:** Now, take your pencil and plot out your life from your birthday and measure the distance until today. Each year should be marked with the date of that year. You will now see a timeline of your time on earth.*

***Step 4:** You should now take your time and in a very relaxed way fill in the key moments of your life. You should label these points using a vertical line and a clear label. The key moments should include, major events and achievements, illness, relationships, work – essentially your highlights AND lowlights.*

***Step 5:** You should now – on the horizontal line – build horizontal blocks and the distance and information within each block should relate to, say your "relationship". If you had a partner for two years, then you should add that to the timeline. If you lived in a certain country or area, you should add that. You will now see overlapping boxes of information. It is very important that you put the low* *points (possible moments of say "depression" etc.). You can do this vertically which should give you more than enough space.*

Step 6: *Your income: go to birth and then draw a line from there until today. You need to create a vertical axis on the left with indicators from say 1 – 10. Then draw a line across the whole timeline indicating to, in your own opinion, what your financial situation was. If you were dead broke one year, then the line should be at zero. If you were rich for ten years, the line can go straight up and stay up for the horizontal distance of 1 metre on the sheet. The line itself will obviously go up and down but should not be disconnected at any point.*

Step 7: *You will now see the key points and moments in your life one gigantic timeline in front of you. You'll see where you have lived, your relationships, your high points and achievements, your low points, time of illness etc. It's important that you do this in pencil because you will start remembering things as you go and might have moments of clarity after you have already made notes.*

The final step: The happiness line

On the left side you need to create a vertical line which is the "happiness and content" measurement – say 20cm vertical. Now you should start your line on the left, at birth, and then draw towards the right…a long long line! Look at all of the information and time on your own timeline and remember when you were happy… when you were happy the line goes up, when you were REALLY happy and content, it goes to the top! If you were down for a sustained period of time or a short period of time, the line should dip. Be honest with yourself and keep going until today! After a few days, take a look at your timeline. Do you notice any patterns of behaviour or anything interesting that you didn't realise about yourself?

Lessons Learned

This exercise alone can teach you more about yourself and tendencies and patterns in your life than any other. Just seeing the links and patterns and how they correspond with your happiness levels might even shock you. It will certainly be a revelation. You will also see how certain relationships and incidents had on your wellbeing. You might note that you were always happy, when you were financially secure and felt down when you were poor. You might see that the happiest time in your life was when you had no money but was working on a piece of art for a year! The point is, for the first time look closely at your life. It will certainly inform you and from now on and will have an incredible subconscious effect on you. It will also remind you that we are only on this earth for a limited period of time.

Chapter 21

PSYCHOLOGICAL DEVICES AND TECHNIQUES

I suspect that most people on the spectrum, if I say, "living in my world" will know exactly what I'm talking about. I really took a substantial amount of time thinking about this issue and how I would address it, in my own way, for myself. However, "address" in actuality means, "attempted address". I visited Berlin, Germany and decided to use the opportunity to test how some psychological devices and mental techniques to see if it could help with this "living in your own world" or "living in a bubble" issue.

The first couple of attempts didn't quite work, but then I worked out something which actually had a substantive impact. Before I explain and tell you all about it I want to tell you about a technique I use when I teach students in dance class, because it relates to what we are talking about today.

Doing Something Physically Impossible

There are some dance moves that I teach that are physically and anatomically impossible to perform. This is because the human body cannot physiologically execute them. With that said, I explain the process and then ask the students to attempt the impossible move and to *imagine* that it's happening. There has never been a single occasion where the physically impossible has been made possible … but something else has happened.

They came close!

The Challenge of Living in a "Bubble"

The one thing which I really focussed on was this idea of **feeling** like I was living in a "bubble". How on earth can we solve that one? It's like you've been placed in a world with lots of people but you have an invisible bubble around you. You want to break out but you can't, as it's physically impossible. You see people walking past and people having their life experiences and you wish you could experience that too… but you can't because you **feel** like you live in your "bubble".

How can you solve that? That's not an easy one to tackle for sure! It took me two years to come up with something that I'm willing to share with you, that I have tested, that I find works for me.

I felt like I made good progress with the "Possible discernment and naivety challenges" and created a mechanism to try and solve that issue. So, I really considered the "bubble" issue in the same way. After two years of many types of mental techniques and psychophysical devices, on a really "low" day, it hit me. It was so obvious too!

How can you escape the inescapable?

Well, you don't, I told myself … you *EMBRACE THE BUBBLE,* that doesn't exist!

Embracing the Bubble and Living in Your Own World

The real "pain" comes from not necessarily "living in a bubble" but ***feeling*** excluded from what's "outside" of that non-existent "bubble". However, this is 100% **psychological and emotional** which means that the *solution* is probably also **psychological and emotional.**

There certainly is no bubble around you separating you from the world. It's a feeling only.

That knowledge alone is extremely empowering. Because it puts YOU back in control. You focus on what YOU can control and not what you can't and that alone is a very powerful psychological device in itself.

The irony is, I found that this route can, in actual fact give you the *feeling* of breaking out of the bubble! It's like a back door route into the world. It takes a little work (but not much), it takes time (but not much) and the most important ingredient of all… it takes ENTHUSIASM and CONFIDENCE!

You will find that the world may well join YOU in your "bubble" because this will be attractive and infectious. However, the mental device is completely counter intuitive. I tested it in Prague, Czech Republic for about five days. I have called my psychological device, "The internal furnace of fulfilment" and it's an internal validation system for you inside your bubble!

The Internal Furnace of Fulfilment

This metaphor is a psychological device designed to help refocus your perspective towards *internal fulfilment* rather than looking for and towards external validation and fulfilment, which helps towards feeling more comfortable within any perceived bubble and indirectly circumvents that same bubble, so that you feel even more connected and less "excluded".

Here is the process and the rules and main points of "The internal furnace of fulfilment":

1) You must have a passion that you can physically occupy your time and attention with, and put your energy into. This must be something that you enjoy and something which is not harmful to anybody or anything. If you don't have one, create one. As previously discussed in this book, it will probably be your passion and area of expertise. You then make a list relevant to your passion. That list should be "impossible" to achieve because it is so long. This is a very good way of shutting down excuses! For example, if you are an expert in World War Two history you may make a list that goes like this:

- *Visit every WW2 museum in your city, then country, then continent, then the world*
- *Read every major WW2 book ever written*
- *Visit every WW2 historical site in your city, then country, then the world*

- *Discover things that have never been discovered before about WW2*
- *Write a book about your experiences and begin to teach about what you have learned*
- *Learn all about the aircraft of WW2. Work out a way to fly in a WW2 aircraft etc.*

You get my point! The list is endless and it cuts off any excuses at source because this excludes the possibility of being "bored" or not having something to "do". Now, in case your brain starts creating more excuses, like financial issues etc. then you can reorder your list to only include free activities first, until you have any required resources. Even then, you will have more than you can possibly achieve. If you need money, you will make money. If you can't work out a way to make money, then return to the free activities until there are no more to do, which is impossible, as you don't have enough decades on earth to even read all of the WW2 or History books in the library which you can borrow for free, for example.

2) You decide in one moment that you will utilise a "The internal furnace of fulfilment". You mentally decide that from now on, your fulfilled comes from inside of you and that source is powered by you and only by you. The

"furnace" is not a real furnace … it's a special one, because the "heat" (i.e. fulfilment, happiness, acceptance, validation) can only come from *your* internal furnace and secondly, the same "heat" generated by your furnace is **non-transferable**. This means that it is unlike real fire. It is completely invalid when it is outside of you and loses its "energy". In the same way somebody can't give you their "heat" from their furnace. This means that it can only be sourced internally. This means:

- *If somebody walks up to you and gives you £100,000,000 in cash, you accept in advance that this cannot give you any "heat" (i.e. fulfilment, happiness, acceptance, validation etc.).*
- *The most beautiful person on earth walks up to you and asks you on a date or to marry you, you accept in advance that this cannot give you any "heat" (i.e. fulfilment, happiness, acceptance, validation etc.).*
- *You are promoted to the CEO of the most valuable company of all time and you accept in advance that this cannot give you any "heat" (i.e. fulfilment, happiness, acceptance, validation etc.).*

- *Anything "nice", "good" or "positive" given to you, externally cannot give you any "heat" (i.e. fulfilment, happiness, acceptance, validation etc.).*

3) You completely embrace your bubble and turn your lens inwards (to ultimately face outwards). This means that you, as extreme as this is going to sound, from now on expect nothing from anybody – regardless of the circumstance. In fact, you do not require acknowledgement or appreciation at all. No matter what you do! **You "do" because it is of intrinsic value and aligned with your "passion" and wellbeing or something you are required to do for the greater good.** The "greater good" is something which is a personal moral decision for you to decide on your own. If you determine that something is morally required or practically required, then do it. If not, don't. If you are selfish, you will remain selfish. If you are generous, you will remain generous. However, everything else which is outside of those exceptions is purely focussed on your passion or to that end. This means:

- *You walk up to a stranger and help them pick up all of their dropped belongings. You do not expect a thanks. You do not expect even a look or the smallest amount acknowledgement. You may accept it but you do not expect it.*

- *You clean your best friend's house, from top to bottom. You do not expect a thanks. You do not expect even a look or the smallest acknowledgement. You may accept it but you do not expect it.*
- *You give away £100,000,000 to a charity. You do not expect thanks. You do not expect even a look or the smallest acknowledgement. You may accept it but you do not expect it.*
- *You engage in a conversation with somebody. You do not expect a reply. You do not expect even a look or the smallest amount of acknowledgement. You may accept it but you do not expect it.*

Everything you do is focussed 100% on advancing your main life passion with the exception of actions which you determine are morally or practically required for the greater good or your own good, within your own personal moral spectrum. To repeat, the action is executed for its intrinsic value only, with zero expectation of acknowledgement or expectation that it will give you any "warmth" or "heat" except the "heat" generated internally from the "power" of the intrinsic action and the heat from that. You do not feel the "need" to speak, communicate or receive anything from anyone, in particular.

How to start a 'Metaphorical Furnace'

When you wake up in the morning, over the duration of this "experiment", the first thing you should do is SMILE. The smile indicates a knowledge that your "heat" is generated internally… and that is GREAT news! Secondly, a physical kick start is required to start a real furnace so we too have a physical kick start to boost our *metaphorical* furnace. Here it is:

1. *As soon as you open your eyes in the morning, you smile.*
2. *As soon as you stand up out of bed you tense your hands, chest and arms and at the same time, in three short burst, expel air through your nose with FORCE. You should add three physical movements.*
3. *Simultaneously, with the three exhalations and forceful "rocking" movements, you internally say "It's IN – SIDE – ME!" If you wish to say it out loud – DO IT!*

Possible Side Effects and Results

If you feel sadness because you feel that you are excluded and live in your bubble then there is no loss in trying a mental technique to try and avoid feeling that way. The worst that can happen is that it doesn't work and that you feel "sadness". With that said, I found that you may feel "sadness" for twenty-four to forty-eight hours when participating in a psychological device like this. However, it's my opinion that this is more to do with "facing" the issue directly. Once you see the positive effects and a short amount of time passes, this will pass and at the worst, even if it didn't work and it's all nonsense, you can resume your usual baseline of "sadness". However, you will be shocked at the impact this technique can have… the positive results were actually shocking to me!

The results were absolutely counter intuitive … and I measured them!

Shocking Results

During the first half of my trip to Prague, Czech Republic I spoke with five people including, the man at the taxi reception desk at the airport and very briefly with the taxi driver, somebody at the accommodation and two waiters. I had no meaningful human interactions than this, over four days. I decided that this was the time to activate my psychophysical device and did so on the fifth morning. I found that the first twenty-four hour or so, were very tough as I felt sadness that it had all resorted to this, however, that soon passed. Then things started happening...

Waiter Number 1

During the first part of the trip I visited Prague Castle multiple times and I ate in the restaurant. I was served by two waiters. During the first part of the trip we spoke but only spoke about logistics. What I wanted to eat and sit etc. However, I returned mid experiment and something very interesting happened. The waiter came up to me in a very friendly enthusiastic manner and greeted me. He asked me if I wanted the same as I had before. I was slightly surprised that he remembered what I wanted. It was a very nice experience and we got talking. We talked in detail about the differences between Prague in summer and Prague in winter. When we were talking, the next table got involved with the conversation.

Waiter Number 2

The routine went like this: I would walk around the castle and then go to the restaurant and eat. I would then walk around the castle and then go to the cafe on the side of the castle wall. After my restaurant experience, I walked to the cafe, which is outside. As I walked up the waiter, smiled and said, "Would you like your usual?" I smiled and said, "Yes, please!" He then added, "I've reserved your usual table and it's waiting for you." We both smiled as it was a small cafe, but he was right, that was the exact table. He explained that they were out of Coca Cola but had a new Schweppes Cola. He explained his thoughts and I tried the new drink. We talked and had a great time.

Return Taxi Journey

I had a very extensive conversation with the taxi driver on the return journey. At the end of the journey he said, "I wish I had more conversations like this one, here is my card, please call me the next time you come to Prague."

At the Airport and Beyond

I have a habit of going to the perfume section when I'm at the airport and testing out the perfumes. I just like the feminine smells. A perfume really does take you back and for me, it links me to, for example, friends or ex-girlfriends etc. I enthusiastically started to smell a perfume, which was the sister perfume of one that my ex-partner used to wear. It actually smelt really nice but not as nice as my ex-partner's version. I was mentally going through all of this in my mind and obviously visually doing so because a beautiful woman walked past and then looked at me, walked towards me and said, "Which one is that? It looks nice". I "woke" from my little internal dialogue with myself and said, "yes", but that she should try the other one, which was better and explained why I wasn't smelling that one, and we both laughed. I then told her that I hope she enjoyed them, as I left her smelling them and off I went. Later as I sat waiting for the plane, she came and sat opposite me.

Before this I found myself in the middle of a wedding being held at the Prague Museum of Technological and quite a few other "random" adventures. I calculated that I had had more than four times the number of the human interactions that the first part of the trip and they were really fun, joyous and interesting conversations! In addition, all of these interactions happened when I was in the middle of following my passion. For example, I was literally working through my Prague list of locations, museums, galleries and places I wanted to go, during which these things happened.

I felt sadness and isolation during the first part of the trip, like I was in the bubble and during the second part of the trip I had such a great time with really meaningful and nice human interaction, which I enjoyed. As I write this, I return to Prague in five days … I enjoyed myself that much.

Enthusiasm and Extending Your Bubble to Include Others

If you walk into a bar, let's say and you are insecure and uncomfortable and feeling like you live in your bubble and order a drink. You, as well as not particularly enjoy the experience, will probably not have any enjoyable human interactions. However, the same "you" walks into a bar, which is linked in some way to your passion i.e., it's en route to a location, or is intrinsically linked histrionically or architecturally to your passion and you enjoy the interest in it for that alone, you will see things will happen!

At the very least you will enjoy the experience because it is aligned with your passion. For example, you walk into a special building with special architecture. You sit down and really take an interest in that architecture and the design of the room and the ergonomics of the table, the set design, the menus etc. Human beings are curious beings and are attracted to enthusiasm! So, when somebody sees YOU having a good time for real, SOMEBODY will want to be part of AUTHENTIC action. Just the same way, if you stand in a busy street and look up, people will look up too! Or stand and point, people will be curious.

At that time, you can explain your passion and at that moment, just for a moment, you have succeeded in extended your bubble to include them ... in a bar! Even if nothing becomes of it, you've had a meaningful conversation, about something you enjoy in a location that is in some way linked to something you're passionate about. That in itself is a great thing and I can guarantee that if you keep doing this, eventually, your circumstances will change and your bubble will grow over time.

Not putting pressure on people or imposing your expectations on them is a VERY ATTRACTIVE THING. They will WANT to be around you if you make this a way of life because you will want nothing and provide enthusiasm, energy and value and be a living example of somebody that is brave enough to follow their passion. You will see… so few people have the courage to do it, that when you do it, you will be "different" and if you already feel "different", then you might as well embrace it and go all the way! In other words, embrace the bubble! That bubble can be your doorway to self-improvement, knowledge and living enthusiastically which can and probably will lead to, not you leaving the bubble but the world joining you inside.

Other Unexpected Benefits

- *You will not tolerate disrespect, time wasters or nonsense any more*
- *Your value of yourself and self-respect levels increase*
- *You become more attractive*
- *You are filled with more enthusiasm*
- *Your contentment levels increase*
- *Your meaningful interactions increase*
- *Become closer to your life goal and passion*
- *You will become more generous and notice the "small" things more*

And last but not least ... 'the 20%'

There is a proportion of people in this world that are real life "heroes". I don't know if the percentage is 20% but I can tell you that these people are the people who have empathy and sensitivity and consideration. They will be the "greens" on your list. Focus on those "greens". Surround yourself with "greens" and invest in *them.*

Your Way Is the Only "Right" Way for You

You can find your own way... you can do it! In a way, nobody can give advice how to discover yourself and what works for you, except you. It's from within. You can evolve based on your own knowledge and experience. You are 100% in charge, you are the captain, YOU are the expert.

You won't get it in full, from this book, or any book because it is your duty and responsibility to create a process or routine or a plan that works for **you** in your life. On the other hand, you will get closer to the destination, regardless, because you can gain knowledge from any book, experience or human being in an apophatic sense. This means that if it doesn't work for *you*, then at least you *know* it doesn't work you. There is much value in even that.

Focus on creating your *own* “guide book” for *yourself* through knowledge and experience.

Good luck!

Source Notes

https://www.autism.org.uk/about/what-is/myths-facts-stats.aspx

http://psychiatryassociatespc.com/doc/Autism_Quotient_Test.pdf

https://psychcentral.com/quizzes/autism-quiz/

https://en.wikipedia.org/wiki/Auditory_verbal_agnosia

https://www.imdb.com/title/tt0717443/

https://network.autism.org.uk/knowledge/insight-opinion/autism-and-eating-issues-interview-dr-elizabeth-shea

https://www.amazon.com/Avoidant-Children-including-Spectrum-Conditions/dp/1785923188

https://en.wikipedia.org/wiki/Autism_spectrum

https://www.imdb.com/title/tt0898266/

https://en.wikipedia.org/wiki/Sociological_imagination

http://www.autismtoolbox.co.uk/understanding-autism/social-imagination/

https://www.ons.gov.uk/peoplepopulationandcommunity/birthsdeathsandmarriages/divorce/bulletins/divorcesinenglandandwales

http://sfhelp.org/

https://www.amazon.com/Whos-Really-Running-Your-Fourth/dp/1456875051

https://www.amazon.com/Eccentrics-Sanity-Strangeness-David-Weeks/dp/0394565657

https://www.washingtonpost.com/archive/lifestyle/1995/10/24/nuts-aboutoddballs/0d09728bf47a-48a9-b31e-80a1e16f8141/?noredirect=on&utm_term=.a2bd89d7ae83

https://www.economist.com/science-and-technology/2009/04/16/genius-locus

https://www.spectrumnews.org/features/deep-dive/extraordinary-minds-the-link-between-savantism-and-autism/

https://www.thedailybeast.com/a-radical-new-autism-theory

https://aspergers101.com/aspergers101-faq/

https://www.harbourguides.com/nautical-sayings/BATTEN-DOWN-THE-HATCHES-ORIGIN

http://www.autism-help.org/autism-high-functioning-hfa.htm

Special Thanks

Dr Cho Cho Khin

Nicky and Collin

Karsten, Hege, Kasper and Taran

Mohammed Nabulsi

Rolfe Klement (Creative Sunshine back cover photography)

Debz Hobbs-Wyatt

Aimee Coveney

Jason and Marina

Therese, Eivind, Ylva and Thuva

Henriette, Belle and Herman

Caroline Saunders

Ole Magne Hundhammer

Ebba the snow assassin

Raie Omoshebi

About the author

Anthony King is a choreographer who started teaching dance at the world-famous Pineapple Dance Studios, London in 2004 and has authored seven books on a variety of subjects, from Dance to Asbergers to Music History. He has taught stars from music, sport and film including Emma Watson, Miss World, Harry Potter, various members of Royalty (European and Middle Eastern), Pink Floyd, Top of the Pops, The Jonathan Ross show, Richard and Judy Show, Britain's Got Talent, BBC's EastEnders, BBC's The Office, and the England Football Team. Choreographed fashion shows for Vidal Sassoon, Anthony has starred in and choreographed commercials for Sony PlayStation, Maverick Media, Warner Music and more. Anthony is the original choreographer of the west end musical, "Thriller Live". Anthony has held dance team building events and workshops for the worlds biggest companies from Twitter to Google, HM Treasury Department, Lego, Capgemini, Anglo American, PwC, Bonnier Publishing, King (creators of Candy Crush), City Sprint, Red Bull, Cisco Systems, TK Maxx, American Express, Proctor & Gamble, Metro

Newspaper group, Rimmel London and many more.He has been interviewed on most of the worlds national and International media including Sky News, BBC News, BBC Breakfast, Channel 4, Channel 5, ITV, ITV 2, CNN, ITN, BBC Radio 1, Capital FM, Choice FM, BBC Radio London and many more. His online lessons have been viewed over 35 million times as well as being featured on YouTube homepage on numerous occasions. His classes have been described by the 'THE SUN' newspaper as 'Hot!' 'Elle girl' magazine have featured his classes as the 'NEXT BIG THING' as well as "dynamic and charismatic" by the London Lite. The Financial Times of London has recommended and featured Anthony's classes and he has been featured as a contributing writer for magazines including 'MORE MAGAZINE' as 'Celebrity dance tutor'.

Anthony King's "Living in a Bubble" Online Consultations

If you'd like to contact Anthony personally with regards to personal online consultations for help, advice or just to talk about any subject from this book please email: info@bubbleasd.com or see bubbleasd.com and anthony-king.com for more details.

Also by the Author

The Personal Development Book for Performers
(coming in 2019)

Dance Like the Stars - updated
(coming in 2019)

Michael Jackson Fact Check -
Fact checking the Michael Jackson "experts"

Michael Jackson and Classical Music

Anthony King's Guide to
Michael Jackson's Dangerous Tour

Anthony King's Guide to
Michael Jackson's History Tour

Printed in Great Britain
by Amazon